SEEDS
OF MAGICK

Catherine Summers and Julian Vayne are
both practising occultists, and have been
working together since 1984. Individually
they have been involved in travelling
abroad, youth work, magazine marketing,
graphic art and tarot counselling. They have
led courses in the tarot and self-awareness,
and have developed a programme of
workshops and lectures in the UK and the
USA. Their primary interest is in the
application of magick in daily life as a tool
for self-awareness, inter-personal
communication, and in an ecological
context. They live in Buckinghamshire with
their son, Seth.

Front cover illustration by Warron Prentice.

SEEDS
OF MAGICK

*An Exposé of Modern
Occult Practices*

Catherine Summers & Julian Vayne

quantum

LONDON • NEW YORK • TORONTO • SYDNEY

quantum

An imprint of W. Foulsham & Co. Ltd.
Yeovil Road, Slough, Berkshire SL1 4JH

ISBN 0–572–01598–4

Copyright © 1990 Catherine Summers & Julian Vayne

Printed in Great Britain at St Edmundsbury Press, Bury St Edmunds

'Everyone has the right to freedom of thought, conscience and religion; this right includes freedom to change his religion or belief, and freedom, either alone or in community with others and in public or private, to manifest his religion or belief in teaching, practice, worship and observance.'

From the Universal Declaration of Human Rights, Article No. 18, as published by the United Nations, to which Britain is a signatory.

This book is dedicated to all those who were there: those who attended the birth and growth of Invoking Earth, and helped it to flourish and change. In particular we would like to thank Steve Winzar, Bran, Jay, Gary Kirkby, Phil Hine, Jane O'Connor, and those who may prefer not to be named but, nevertheless, were there. We also make a dedication to those we taught and learnt from, the core group of RootMagick and all those of Dark Star. This book is for all our friends, everywhere, past, present, and future.

CONTENTS

INTRODUCTION

This book is divided into four sections. The first discusses the history of magick, particularly in relation to the Western occult tradition. The second section explains the problems that have grown up in occultism and how they have been reflected in religion and society. The third section contains information on the nature of magickal power and occult 'secrets'. It gives our (but not the only) solutions for these difficulties, the results of our research and subsequent construction of the magickal form that we call 'Serket'. This third part is based around the transcripts of four particular rituals. The fourth section of the book contains more background and detailed practical information on magick.

We ask the reader to pay most attention not to the rituals but to the chapters that precede and follow them. Ritual is only one method of expressing occult truth, and is most certainly not the only way. It is also not the wording of a rite that is of primary importance but the magickal knowledge and wisdom that is held by its writer and participants. Ritual is an aspect of magick but not an end in itself.

Because occultism is a complete system of knowledge, it is difficult to isolate certain statements of magickal truth without including all the necessary qualifications. This difficulty is particularly true in attempting to define the nature of a particular reality. We have used reasonable generalisations for the sake of brevity when dealing with these concepts but the seasoned occultist will also be aware of the finer points within these laws which we do not discuss.

Our work is not intended to produce an established litany but we do hope to inspire honest free-thinking occultism.

There are many problems facing magick today, some of which we deal with in this book. These problems must be overcome before any work can be done on integrating the purpose of the present Aeon into the evolving collective mind of humanity.

Today, societies all across the globe are experiencing a state of drastic upheaval. The first shock waves of a change in social structure are beginning to take effect. The cause of this, from a magickal perspective, is the present shift from one Aeon into another. An Aeon is a period of time, approximately 2200 years, calculated from the circling 'wobble' of the earth's axis. During each Aeon, humanity undergoes a change in consciousness on a religious, magickal, technical, social and political basis.

At present we are passing out of the Aeon known to occultists as the 'Osiris Aeon', that is to say the age of the patriarchal god force. The approaching Aeon represents a double force. The incoming current is neither male nor female; it is balanced power. The male counterpart of this energy is represented by Horus, the divine Son (symbolic of the individual), and the goddess Ma'at, who represents truth and justice (symbolic of the group). More about this 'double Aeon' can be found in the works of Kenneth Grant, Aleister Crowley, and others.

The information we present is designed to demonstrate the magickal ideals and structure necessary to use this balanced current. The rituals are the fruits of our research drawn together to provide a practical framework. They are intended to show how the concepts can have a practical application.

Our formulation of magick, Serket, is a particularly potent occult form. Whilst we would be interested to hear from those who have undertaken to use this method, we would counsel prudence when working with it. Magick is not a subject that can be studied 'nine to five'. To be successful it must become an integral part of one's whole life, and great respect and care must be taken before using a system, such as Serket, which can tap some of the deepest levels of the Self.

Serket is not just another occult faction. It is one face of a universal expression which directly addresses the present need for humanity to take control of its own evolutionary destiny.

We explore the ideas of occultism as a whole, and our expression of these concepts embodied in our magickal system, Serket.

The word Serket is a multi-compound noun, rooted in the ancient Egyptian language. It contains the word 'Serk', the name of the goddess of the circle (an aspect of Sekhmet, or Maut). Also, it contains the name of the dark god, Set. The word Serket is also directly related to the name of the goddess Seket, or Serqet, the scorpion queen, who represents the forces of putrefaction and regeneration. Serket is also an anagram of the word 'Sekret' (secret), the importance of which will be apparent to those involved in what is mistakenly known as 'left-hand path' occultism.

Serket developed from the work of a group known as 'Invoking Earth', which was founded in 1981. This was set up as an open magickal group designed to help dispel the mists of malpractice and misunderstanding surrounding occultism today.

To begin with, Invoking Earth was non-hierarchical but it soon became apparent that some form of leadership structure was needed. It also rapidly became obvious that some type of teaching system was required. We then formulated a training system, including various exercises for the would-be occultist, pathworking, and practical magickal information. The basis of this teaching system is included in later chapters.

Meanwhile, on the magickal side, we began to adapt the basic Alexandrian Craft rituals for our own use. We soon began investigating other magickal paths and drawing on information held in other mythological forms. This rewriting of ritual was not done for any dogmatic reasons. It was obvious to us that much Wiccan ritual is confused and incomplete, and that a less parochial view with regard to changing and performing ritual was necessary.

Invoking Earth moved to the Lincolnshire countryside in 1984, and it was here that we began to sort out our ideas, drawing them together to form an internally consistent system. Serket's basic structure was born out of both logic and inspiration drawn from our work with Tantric arts.

It has been in a constant state of flux since its formulation, for while its basic matrix remains stable, other ideas and forms have been absorbed into it as necessary. Our expression of this current, in terms of the Sabbats, is contained herein.

Occultists must open the dusty recesses of their art, and remove the clutter of outmoded mumbo jumbo that is at present obscuring the flame of magick. Why should the occultist complicate matters by using convoluted symbolism and dead languages in a rite, when the True Will, focused by a straightforward act, can accomplish the same goal? Magick does not lose power by a return to the simplicity advocated here. As we hope to show, Serket, and any allied magickal form, is as profound as any other esoteric path.

All that is presented herein is based on experience and recognition of esoteric laws which can be recognised by all. It is not our intention simply to rebuke the occult world but nor are the problems, esoteric laws and possible solutions postulated, mere supposition.

This book is not a 'how to' grimoire, but we would ask the reader to consider the possibility of using the concepts, if not the actual rites set forth, in his or her own esoteric work.

Readers will find an extensive Bibliography on page 180. This will enable particular books and references mentioned in the text to be traced easily, as well as forming a basis for further reading.

CHAPTER 1
ROOTS OF THE CRAFT

'To observe the Invisible one must first learn to observe the Visible.'
Ancient Qabalistic maxim

THE PRE-HISTORY OF MAGICK

In order to understand the present and possible future of the Craft movement, and indeed occultism in general, the conglomeration of past magickal systems which have formed the foundation of modern Wicca must be understood. The term 'Craft movement' today covers a multitude of different groups and belief systems ranging from purely religious paganism through to exclusively magickal groups. However, virtually all occult systems contain a common seed of truth, a thread which can be traced back to an original source.

Research into the prehistory of magick is difficult but there are indications as to the nature of early occult thought. One of these clues is the recurrence of various symbols and concepts in the magiculture of vastly different societies. For example, the symbol of the serpent occurs in every mythological system, even in North Eskimo culture in places uninhabited by snakes! Other clues are given away by the recurrence of symbols such as the pentagram (from such diverse locations as Southern India, China and Europe), the spiral, and so on. Many of these images come from archetypal forms which permeate every culture but perhaps the best source of information is simply to be had by studying the lifestyle of these peoples. Magick grew from necessity not whim. Survival was paramount and only patterns of thought and behaviour that could be beneficial in the evolutionary struggle were incorporated into these cultures.

As Don Juan points out to Carlos Casteneda, 'In a world where death is the hunter, my friend, there is no time for regrets or doubts. There is only time for decisions.'

In the following pages we have utilised both historical information and also this 'intuitional logic' to form a picture of what early occultism was like.

Many of the theories and practices that are still used in occultism date back to early hunter/gatherer cultures. Life was bound up in the turn of the seasons in the migrational and reproductive cycles of the animals the tribe hunted, the growth of plants whose fruits were harvested. Society had to store food through the winter months and hunt frequently — agriculture was yet to develop. Life was harsh and the tribe had to cooperate closely, sharing knowledge and resources in order to survive. It is important to remember that these cultures were widely distributed around the globe. People evolved in equatorial Africa and migrated into three main areas. These were Eastern Asia, the Americas, and the European landmasses. The problems faced by these people differed in relation to climatic conditions but many problems remain common to all.

Humanity has survived because of its ability to adapt. Whilst most animals can only adapt to a situation by physically changing their bodies, human beings adapt mentally. The human was placed in a seemingly impossible situation. Devoid of protective body hair, unable to afford self-protection with claws or fangs, the whole biological structure was seemingly doomed to extinction. This difficult situation forced man to adapt by mental evolution. Humanity developed clothing, learnt how to use fire and how to trap and hunt down animals for food. The physically stronger Neanderthal peoples died out to be replaced by their physically weaker but mentally stronger relations, Homo sapiens.

With the mental evolution that led to the development of tools, abstract concepts and ideas about the nature of the universe also began to be formulated. It is important to remember that no idea evolved that was not useful to the tribe. These cultures lived in a situation where extinction may have been one poor hunting season away. Nothing became part of pre-historic society unless it could be practically applied to the common good with 'tangible' results.

In pre-Druidic society, the concepts we now refer to as religion, belief, and magick, were not considered separate from everyday existence. There was no veil dividing their physical reality from the realms of magickal reality. The magickal knowledge of the tribe was held by the Shaman, who was chosen on merit, not because of their birth to any particular favoured individual. Certain outward characteristics may have led to an individual adopting the role of Shaman: epilepsy (still a common qualification for the African Shaman) or unusual colouring (red hair or albinoism) are examples. Early people noticed how psychic power was often most active in such people.

The Shaman had to be the repository of wisdom because information had to be passed by word of mouth or rudimentary symbols. The attitude towards the Shaman was one of respect (as one should have for any individual who uses their talents to the full, whatever they might be) not fear. He or she worked with a power which though unseen was a natural part of the environment and was not considered supernatural. The Shaman was part of the tribe and added skill to the hunting and healing abilities possessed by other tribe members. Shamanistic power related to everyday existence and was not aloof from it. In a meritocratic society it was only because of the practical *necessity* of Shamanistic knowledge that a member of the tribe could be spared to develop psychic skills rather than go out hunting.

During this period, magick as a force was accepted without question. The reason for this was that, in order to survive in their harsh environment, the tribe's members had to be constantly alert. Their physical senses had to be always on the look out for things that could be useful, or for situations which could harm them. This high state of awareness allowed the psychic perceptions to develop as an extension of the physical senses.[1]

The tribe was a close-knit family-like unit where each member was interdependent on others for survival. As in a family, one member would instinctively know when another was in trouble. The group formed the first gestalt, a group mind that (particularly in the early stages of language) acted as a reservoir of knowledge, and provided a telepathic link between all the tribe members.[2] To these people psychic perception was normal. They had access to the invisible, and so the Shaman as a specialist in these realms was no more abnormal than the individual who specialised in flint knapping or hunting. Everyone could tap the psychic reality. It was probably this that accounted for the vast array of astonishing leaps in understanding that led to many early innovations and inventions. These people had access to what occultists call the Akashic record, the astral repository of all knowledge past and future.

Flashes of inspiration come when individuals are opened up to these realms, and the information received manifests in conscious knowledge. In modern times one well known example is that of the scientist August Kekulé who discovered the structure of the benzene molecule. While awake he was unable to produce a satisfactory model of benzene's molecular structure. Upon falling asleep he dreamt of a serpent swallowing its own tail, then of carbon and hydrogen atoms floating in a circular pattern which changed into the ring-like structure of the benzene molecule. Upon waking, Kekulé found he knew how the atoms linked together.

Ideas like the flint axe, perhaps inspired by a flash of 'Akashic illumination', may appear simple to us but for

18

prehistoric man such an innovation was entirely revolutionary. To truly appreciate the complexity of such an invention one must remember that more sophisticated modern devices are more often variations on a theme. To put it in perspective, when was the last time you made something completely original using only nature as your source of materials and tools?

Because of their way of life, these people had to remain in tune with the seasons or risk extinction. They had to know when different food sources would be available, when the food stores had be full ready for the oncoming winter, and so on. It is unlikely they had any sort of Sabbat celebration in the sense that modern Wicca does. It is probable however that the concept of ritual would develop in response to psychological and practical needs. The importance in ritual is shown by the way it occurs in nature as a declaration of intent, such as the courting behaviour of birds, or the communication of information, as in the comb dance of a honey bee.

Humans too are ritualistic animals constructing ritualistic patterns to draw people together and formulate a group mind. This need for ritual is demonstrated in William Golding's novel, *Lord Of The Flies*, in which a group of schoolboys, marooned on an island, develop their own ritual in response to their needs and original memories. Shamanistic ritual probably involved the use of sympathetic magick: these rites were born from the knowledge that magick does work, not as many writers suppose from group insecurity about the future.

Early people, though living a difficult existence, understood both intuitively and intellectually the concept of the cycle. Each year, they witnessed the vegetation die and grow back, they saw the sun rise and fall, and the waxing and waning of the moon. In each instance they saw the return of these elements in a renewed form. This, coupled with the knowledge of other dimensions of reality, led them to an understanding of reincarnation.

Much Shamanistic knowledge was integral with the belief in spirit contact with the ancestors of the tribe. This is not the communication with individual departed spirits, as in spiritualism, but the exploration of the collective unconscious of the group. To this day, in Africa the elders of the tribe are still given respect and the most important role in tribal society. They believe that without this their spirit will be lost. These concepts meant that the survival of the tribe became more important than that of the individual. This was akin to the later Celtic concept of rebirth. Celtic warriors were certain of their own spirit's immortality, and for this reason were unfearing in the face of death. It was during this period of human evolution that the symbol of the circle or spiral emerged. The spiral represents the cycle of each incarnation in an eternal progression. The maze dances of later cultures have their roots in the same understanding.

Sabbats and other celebratory rites evolved later. They were intended to keep people in touch with the tides of the seasons, as society became more technologically advanced, and more divorced from the patterns of birth, life, death and rebirth.

As we have said, early tribal society was a meritocracy choosing people who were best suited to a particular job irrespective of gender or lineage. However, the emphasis was more often than not placed on a woman of the tribe because she was the one who insured the tribe's continuity through the miraculous process of childbirth. The process was considered miraculous because paternity was not understood. Early cultures did not have many of our modern sexual taboos. Because of this, the mental connection between the male's role in sexual intercourse and the later birth of a child was not realised. Some 'primitive' tribes still do not have a word for 'father' as to them this concept is non-existent. This is evident, for example, in the Trobriand language of north-west Melanesia.

The first deity of early cultures was the Great Mother who

brought forth life. The Great Mother, like the power of shamanistic magick was a real force, not an intellectual idea. She was the first human archetype. The personification of the life force was female because it was through woman that life was created. The goddess was identified with the earth, the sky, the sea, and like these forces she contained the power of destruction as well as creation. The goddess brought forth life, nourished and sustained it, and finally reabsorbed it prior to the secret process of rebirth.

It is necessary at this stage to draw a distinction between the respect paid to the force of the Great Mother, and worship in the conventional sense of the word. Prehistoric people could, for example, look at a volcano and see a natural force both destructive and creative. The volcano was not considered evil or good, it simply *was*, and like any part of the universe was woven into the eternal cycle of existence.

The Great Mother developed different aspects — firstly into two, then four faces. This was in keeping with an increasingly analytical mentality, and both intuitional and logical understanding of duality. Primitive people saw the duality of life, summer/winter, moon/sun, earth/sky. The Great Mother was divided into her 'light' aspect of creation, and 'dark' aspect of destruction. Later the goddess became likened to the phases of the moon or sun, and this linked her specifically to the phases of the moon. The waxing moon, the full moon, the waning moon, and the dark moon, were symbols of her four faces.

With the origin of the female goddess archetype so the second godform began to evolve. The tribal Shaman became more of a magickian in the sense of an occultist, a mercurial figure who we know today in the archetypal Hermes, messenger of the gods. It is important to note that the Shaman, though often referred to as being male, was probably either hermaphroditic or, more likely bisexual.

The magickian (Shaman) appears in all myths and in each displays these dual sexual characteristics. The androgynous Shaman arose both as a personification of shamanistic

21

power and as an attempt to encompass the duality of male and female in one image. The symbolism of the Shaman is illustrated in the use of the 'she-male' in occultism and folklore. Such trans-sexual symbolism as men dressing in women's clothing, is of great antiquity. Often the she-male carried a besom, another symbol of the magickian's duality. Charles and Cherry Lindholm note, 'The shaman's attire makes him appear to be neither man nor woman, but rather a living metaphor for his mediating role as a highly respected healer, who stands between man and the spirit world. In this case cross-dressing is more a ritual than a psychological act, the uniform goes with the job.' Baphomet the 'Goat of Mendes', whom the Knights Templar were accused of worshipping, is also a symbol of this union of male and female as are Mercury, Lucifer, Set, Pan and indeed, at their roots, most male godforms.

Having formulated the Great Mother archetype and that of the Shaman (which in a sense is a subdivision of the former prototype) the image of the god developed. It is likely that the importance of the male representative of power grew when people began the domestication of animals to provide the tribe with a constant source of meat, milk, wool, and so on. The relationship between intercourse, pregnancy, and birth of offspring, began to be understood. Another aspect of the god power was the deification of the hunted animal that was to become the horned god. This is identical to the way certain Red Indian peoples venerated the buffalo. In his book, *The Meaning of Witchcraft*, Gerald Gardner explains another role of the Horned God: 'The Horned God had another function besides being the provider of food. He was also the dealer of death.

It was after his magical dance that the great stag was brought low. One day, the hunter knew, he too must leave this world by the gate of death.' The god archetype then was one of fertilisation and sacrifice. The horned god fertilised the goddess that she might bring forth life. When he became unable to fulfil this role of impregnation he was killed, and his office was replaced by his own offspring. This biological chain formed the basis of the myth of the eternal goddess, and waxing and waning god, which features in every culture: Egyptian, Aztec, Christian, Sumerian, and more. The myth of the 'dying god' has been treated at length in many other texts both magickal and mythological, and more information may be gleaned from these sources, and the complex and yet profoundly simple psychology of this cycle is dealt with in Chapter 4, 'Secrets of Sexuality' (see p. 56).

Another aspect of the sacrificial mythos grew when a society developed agriculture. Part of the custom of giving back an offering of the harvest to the land originated in the need to reseed the earth for the following year. The ritual sprinkling of grain upon the earth was done not in an attempt to placate the earth but rather to sacrifice part of the harvest so there would be grain the following year. There was a deeply symbiotic relationship with their environment. People were aware that they lived within the pattern of a cycle. They therefore took from the earth and made offerings to it, in the form of seed or fertilising matter, in the certainty that they would be repaid. Sacrifice was not waste, it was based on the understanding that you don't get something for nothing.

THE DEVELOPMENT OF RELIGION

As tribal culture grew, both in numbers and complexity, the shamanic figure was replaced by a priesthood, which was in general divorced from the majority of the population.

This metamorphosis was exemplified by the druidic cult of the early Celts. The information available on occult practices at this time is incomplete owing to the Roman invasion of Britain (55 BC – 410 AD) and the subsequent outlawing of the druids, who were both political and religious leaders.

23

The druids also preserved an oral tradition of law, genealogies and magick in the same way as the tribal Shaman. Much information was destroyed in the massacre of the druids by the Roman general, Suetonius Paulinus, and the later destruction of the famous Bangor library by the Roman Christian Church. The druids were one of the first groups in Britain to institute the idea of a popular religion, whilst themselves retaining the instinctive understanding of magick as well as using more complex scientific occult methods, such as geomancy, astrology, and the magick of the written word. Druidic knowledge incorporated information from other systems from as far afield as the Mediterranean, Egypt, and India, carried along trading routes that ran from these areas to Britain with its deposits of copper and tin, one of the reasons that many common factors can be found in the 'technical' occult traditions of these different areas.[3]

The druids developed a heliocentric theory of reincarnation, believing that the human spirit incarnated in different elemental forms on different planets: for example a watery body on Venus, an airy body on Mercury, and as fire of spirit in the sun. They used the Asiatic idea of symbolising the god and goddess archetypes as forms of the sun and moon. The druids did not worship these bodies, they saw them as symbols of an overall Creator/Creatorix. In the same way, the Egyptians regarded the ape as the symbol of the god Thoth and not as divine in itself. Most cultures of this period retained the idea that the life force was neither male nor female.

Many other mythologies influenced Britain's occult heritage, including those of the Romans, the Vikings, and the cult of Mithras, and of the Qabalah.

The Romans tended to regard the Celtic gods as directly related to their own deities, however this was primarily for political, rather than philosophical reasons. The Roman mythos, already heavily influenced by Greek culture, absorbed Celtic forms to produce an amalgam of beliefs, many of which persisted in Britain after the Romans left in AD 410.

The Vikings too left their mark, with the Norse images of Valhalla, Hel, and the mythology of Odin's ordeal on the World Ash where he received magickal knowledge in the form of the runes. The incorporation of Norse myths rooted firmly the concept of the warrior cult in Britain. The infiltration of Norse ideas was a gradual process because Viking raids and the following settlements were sporadic rather than uniformly centralised and organised, as was the Roman conquest.

Shortly before the fall of Rome, the Mithras cult arrived. This had evolved in Persia and was popularised as a contemporary of Christianity. Mithras was important because this was the first time that Britain was presented openly with a purely male heroic god figure, with little mention of the goddess. The Mithras cult also brought with it the ideas of Zoroaster, a Persian religious teacher. Zoroaster saw the world as a battle between the forces of good and evil, he further personified these forces and paved the way for the patriarchal God/Devil theology. The concept of good and evil was, as we have shown above, virtually non-existent before this philosophy. Unfortunately because of changing social values (and on an occult level the dawning of the magickally misunderstood Aeon of the God force), this all-male current was readily accepted and formed the basis on which the later Christian myths were to flourish. The concept of 'brotherly love' encouraged by this cult offered a successful alternative to the 'heterosexual' culture of the tribal system in which women were at least equal if not exalted.

The emergence of Christianity came with the Romano/British slave trade. It was a cult promising a glorious hereafter to the impotent masses and a release from the horror of everyday existence. Celtic Christianity was the first centralised form of this belief, brought to Britain, it is believed, by Joseph of Aramethea. Although Celtic Christianity accepted a god as overall creator, the goddess was still acknowledged, and women were ordained as priestesses.

The later Roman form of Christianity, instituted by St Paul and St Augustine, began the steady decline of the importance of women, and therefore of the goddess. Christianity prevented women being actively involved in the cult and suppressed rather than absorbed other beliefs (particularly those of magick). By 824 AD women were forbidden to serve at the altar or give communion. The gods of the old became the devils of the new, and magick became identical with the word anarchy. Christian temples were built on earlier pagan sites and festival dates were calculated to coincide with earlier celebrations, such as All Soul's Eve, which occurs on the same date as the pagan festival of Samhain. By doing this, the church could monitor any religious activity and keep it well under papal control.

The more orgiastic or magickal celebrations of Britain were banned. *Liber Poenitentialis* of Theodore published in the 7th century forbids the practice of dancing in 'animal masks', especially those of 'horned beasts'. Christianity began to become a facade for political and economic gain by those in its elite. The development of a strong church hierarchy severed the link between the priesthood and the people. Some remnants of pre-Christian belief remained but much knowledge was lost and Sabbat festivals degenerated into simple folk custom.

Healing lore was still passed on mainly amongst the women of village communities. Midwives remained outside the church's control because of their involvement with healing, laying out the dead and the secret mystery of birth. They began to function in a way similar to the early tribal Shaman. As women involved with the cycles of birth and death, they were frowned upon by Christianity and were often feared rather than respected for their knowledge. It was the wise woman who remained the last symbol of the goddess and slowly developed into the archetype of the witch. In this role she provided both medicines and poisons, and probably had an understanding of magickal techniques, the use of poppets, folk charms, and divination.

A similar phenomenon occurred within the circles of authority and the establishment, among the alchemists and court magicians. Alchemy was probably the result of druidic understanding, which concealed much occult knowledge under the thin veneer of Gnostic Christianity and the search for the ability to transmute base metals into gold. This transmutation was an overt allegorical reference to the esoteric elevation of the alchemist's spirit.

Occult knowledge began to become High Magick, which demanded a correspondingly high degree of learning and personal wealth in order to obtain the equipment necessary for its practice. The result was that this form of magick was practised mainly by members of the Christian priesthood who were themselves influenced by the Christian mythos. It is probable that some of the priests involved in High Magick became Satanists as a logical reaction to the fact that they saw the material gains available from an alliance with the 'power of evil'.

In an early book by Grillot de Givry called *Witchcraft, Magic and Alchemy*, the author says, 'It is perfectly logical that certain men . . . having seen that God possessed His rich and honoured church on earth . . . should have asked themselves — above all, if they believed that they had a right to complain to God, who had condemned them to a wretched state of life and denied them worldly goods — should they not be the priests of Satan's dominion who would perhaps, give them what God did not deign to give?'

This idea would have been confirmed by two other factors. Firstly, that many priests were engaged in activities they themselves deplored, including Satanism. Secondly, the common people would have seen the church's Satan as a godform containing elements of their old gods and goddesses. Being still unused to the church's new Zoroastrian good/evil doctrine, they would have flocked to this cult. It is interesting to note that the figure who presided over the Witches' Sabbat wore a horned headress and took the lead

27

in the obligatory orgy at the height of the ceremony. Many legends point to the leader being a woman with an artificial penis, usually of wood or bone. Statements that suggest this can be found in many records of witch trials. Isabel Goudie's spontaneous confession, in 1662, stated that, 'His members are exceedingly great and long . . . I found his nature as cold within me as spring-well water.'

This rite developed from the racial memory of the archetypal bisexual Shaman. The amount of intercommunication between these underground groups is unknown but the figure of a wandering priest, the man in black who acted as a messenger between them, possibly with similar bisexual characteristics, is mentioned.

The Christian church also attacked the lingering rites held in honour of the goddess. As early as 1300, the church document called the *Canon Episcopi* mentions the common belief that, 'certain abandoned women perverted by Satan' flew through the air 'with the pagan goddess Diana'.

It was with the Papal Bull of Pope Innocent III, in 1484, that the church began its campaign of torture and oppression, the witch hunts. In Europe alone, an estimated 500 000 people were hanged, drowned or burnt, in order to create scapegoats for the church. Other groups which the church wished to destroy, such as the Cathar heretics and the Jews, who also retained some esoteric knowledge, were persecuted alongside the 'witches'.

The Christians, or more accurately those who perverted the original Christian teachings, harnessed the fear people had of those involved in sorcery, however simplistic in its methods, and the jealousy felt against a section of society who were above the law and beyond the control of the church. This hysteria was accelerated by the publication of *Malleus Maleficarium*, in 1486.

The confusion caused by the rift between the Catholic and Protestant churches, forced home by Henry VIII, created a short period in which officially sanctioned religious persecution diminished, at least as far as witchcraft was concerned. Court magicians gained royal patronage, the king now ruled the church, not vice versa, and allowed occult practices as long as he could control them and use them to further his own aims. In spite of this change of attitude, the social position of women remained unchanged. This is illustrated by the execution of Anne Boleyn because her crime of alleged adultery was considered synonymous with witchcraft.

It was during the reign of Queen Elizabeth I that court magick really gained in importance. This was the first time in many years that a woman had control of an undivided Britain, with a religious policy of relative tolerance. She was the 'Virgin Queen' a symbol of the goddess, and with her ascendency acknowledgement of the occult arts began to return.[4] Astrology, Greek and Roman myths (frequently alluded to in plays of the time, such as those by Shakespeare), the Qabalah, and High Magic, were condoned by the Queen and accepted by the majority. During this period there was also a lively trade in love philtres, popular divination (scrying, palmistry, etc.) and poisons which were in particular demand in the courts of Europe. Elizabeth I was also the patron of Dr John Dee (1527–1608) who was a royal secret agent, astrologer, inventor and famed occultist. In association with Edward Kelly, Dee evolved the Enochian language which is still used in magick today.

Despite Elizabeth's reign, Britain's power structure continued to be patriarchal.

Many of the skills previously held only by village wise women passed into the hands of male physicians who even took over the task of midwifery. Much of the biological and human knowledge used by the wise woman was forgotten and physiological, particular sexual functions became divorced for real people. In 1604, following the freedom of Elizabeth's reign, James I instituted his Witchcraft Act, and added his famous mistranslation/forgery to the Bible, 'Thou shalt not suffer a witch to live' (Exodus, 22:18).

During the following 80 years of the 17th century an

estimated 40 000 people were executed in England and Wales. The witch hunts on the continent grew to new heights, the worst area being Germany in which a special prison, the Hexenhaus, was built in 1627 for the detainment and torture of suspects. In Britain, Matthew Hopkins, the infamous Witchfinder General, made his living instilling terror as the church felt necessary.

Towards the beginning of the 18th century, the craze started to diminish. The reign of George II saw the repeal of the Witchcraft Act in its old form, and the institution of a rewritten law which allowed prosecution of those who pretended to supernatural powers.

THE OCCULT REVIVAL

In 1848, in America, Modern Spiritualism evolved, founded by the Fox sisters. From this tenuous step, magick and the growth of interest in the occult began to increase rapidly.

The late 1800s saw the beginnings of the Golden Dawn, the Rosicrucian orders, and those groups using the teachings of Eliphas Levi. Of all these new orders, it was the Golden Dawn that was to have the most effect on occult sciences in general.

During this period, other advances were taking place in the field of psychology and science. The emergence of both Freudian and Jungian theory were also to influence the Western occult tradition.

At this time all occult groups relied on ancient formulae of magick. The Theosophical Society relied on Eastern mystical techniques but omitted such elements as Tantra, which Blavatsky denounced as 'Black Magick'. The Golden Dawn founded its techniques in classical Qabalism, the teachings of the Rosicrucian orders and Eliphas Levi. The Golden Dawn was extremely hierarchical and its major figurehead, MacGregor Mathers claimed to draw his authority from a group of incarnate adepts known as the 'secret chiefs'. It was this highly regimented system which was, perhaps suprisingly, to produce some of the most advanced occultists of this period.

Alan Bennett, who was once a member of the Golden Dawn, was responsible for introducing many Indian occult concepts to the West, and laid the ground for the study of Tantra. Another one time fellow of the Golden Dawn was Aleister Crowley. Crowley's life and magick is too diverse and complex to explain here and has already been examined in a number of other books (see Bibliography, p. 180). Crowley expounded a branch of occultism he called 'Thelema' which was based on two philosophies which permeate the magickal world. Firstly, popularisation: his system which, though complex in its formulation, became the basis of Wicca, one of the most 'open-ended' occult paths. Secondly, experiment: Crowley expounded a doctrine of change. He advocated experiment in all facets of magick, absorbing useful elements and disregarding those found to be impractical or unhelpful. Even today, much of Crowley's work is still dramatically misunderstood which is hardly surprising as much of his writing is still generally ahead of its time. Crowley was involved with Gerald Gardner, collaborating with him in evolving the *Book of Shadows* which exists in innumerable forms throughout today's Craft groups.

Gerald Gardner was a folklorist, pioneer naturist and author of some of the first practical books on witchcraft and paganism. His first book, ostensibly a work of fiction, was published under the pen-name of 'Scire' in 1949, two years before the repeal of the Witchcraft Act. Gardner claimed to have been initiated into a coven in the New Forest. It is patently obvious however that much of the supposedly 'traditional' ritual had been synthesised from the writings of Crowley, Gardner himself, sections of Dion Fortune's occult novels, and later poetry by Doreen Valiente, combined with earlier sources such as the *Carmena Gadelica* and *Aradia*.

31

Dion Fortune (1891–1946) was another occultist of note who wrote many works which, because of the moral climate of her time had to be toned-down. She was the founder of the Society for Inner Light and was another occultist active during this magickal renaissance. It is important to bear in mind the rate of change at this time both in magickal and social terms. Free thinkers such as Huxley, Shaw, Byron and others, contributed to these changes, gradually stripping away prudish Victorian values. The suffragette movement began the slow task of reawakening society to realise the importance of women in this new era. The emergence of Wicca was yet another part of society's redevelopment.

It is probable that Crowley intended Wicca to act as a popularised OTO (a German magickal order which Crowley attempted to reform along Thelemic lines). A hint of this is given in a letter published in *The Great Beast*, a biography of Crowley edited by John Symmonds.

It seems that Gardner intended the Craft system to reintroduce the oracular priestesses, such as the Delphic pythoness, to serve as the channels through which the new age of magick could be brought to birth.

Both Crowley and Gardner attempted to engineer the beginnings of Wicca to their individual aims. Whether it was their intention that Wicca should become so widely accessible is unknown.

It was in the 1950s that Jack Braceland, who was involved in Gardner's original coven, allegedly circulated the previously highly secret *Book of Shadows*. In the 1960s, magick began to make real developments. The '60s and early '70s saw the growth of experimentation in many fields. Magick evolved alongside the new drug culture and changes of morality. It was during this period that Alex Sanders obtained a transcript of the *Book of Shadows*. Sanders has been frowned upon because he attempted to introduce more of a magickal element into the Craft. Wicca had become mainly religious, concentrating on spiritual devotion and avoiding more practical occult fields. Sanders attempted to introduce

Qabalah into Wicca, however many of the concepts behind magick remained untouched.

The Alexandrian movement grew rapidly in these changing times and for the first time Wicca was open for all to see. During the '60s, Alex and Maxine Sanders had many books and articles published featuring them; they initiated many people and even held open 'stage' circles. Publicity being what it is, not all that was written was favourable or indeed true, and many witches who claim initiation and training from this period have done little to help. This situation, combined with those who claim titles without knowledge, has resulted in the Alexandrian movement degenerating, but without Sanders many occultists would never have found magick, and many good witches would never have been. Important also from these times are Janet and Stewart Farrar. Farrar, originally a journalist, went to interview Sanders, became interested and was initiated. Eventually the Farrars, who became magickal partners, left the main group and have since contributed many excellent books and articles to the Craft movement.

Over the past twenty years an unfortunate fringe has grown up around more reputable occultists and orders but at the same time there has been excellent research carried out into many occult fields. Occultists have found it amusing to note how the new science of quantum physics is discovering concepts which have long been the basis of magick.

This chapter concludes our synopsis of the events which have formed the basis of Wicca and the occult today. We have attempted to give a clear over-view and realise much information, for necessary brevity, has been simplified or omitted. Other factors have influenced the Craft, notably the movements (such as 'feminist' groups) in Germany, the USA, and to a lesser extent Australia. This rich history has thrown up a wealth of information and a vast creative potential for the future of magick. Sadly large numbers of people, including many occultists, have an incomplete knowledge of many facts about the occult. We will analyse these problems in the next chapter.

Footnotes to Chapter 1

1   One of the major contentions of Serket and other similar occult systems is that magickal abilities of whatever type can be developed by the cultivation of the basic five senses to a fine peak. This is the reverse of asceticism, which attempts to gain these powers by the denial of the senses.

2   An example of this phenomenon is that of the Japanese macaque monkeys, a species which exhibits a form of inter-tribal 'psychic' link.

3   These trade routes are demonstrated by the cosmopolitan nature of the grave goods found in the Sutton Hoo site in England. This same excavation also demonstrates the way that many archaeologists have failed in their historical interpretation because of their limited view in relation to ancient religious culture and social ethics.

4   It seems that whenever Britain is under the rule of a queen rather than a king occultism becomes increasingly tolerated and makes great advances. This is apparent in the reign of Elizabeth I (John Dee and the Enochia), Queen Victoria (Crowley and Thelema) and the present revival under the rulership of Queen Elizabeth II.

CHAPTER 2

LIFTING THE VEIL

'The order was deliberately reversed . . . not by the true sages. By the false illuminati and by all the other White Brotherhoods and Rosicrucians and Freemasons and whatnot who didn't really understand the truth and therefore wanted to hide the part of it they did understand. They felt threatened; the real sage is never threatened. They spoke in symbols and paradoxes, like the real sages, but for a different reason. They didn't know what the symbols and paradoxes meant. Instead of following the finger that points to the moon, they sat down and worshipped the finger itself. Instead of following the map, they thought it was the territory and tried to live in it. Instead of reading the menu, they tried to eat it. Dig? They had the levels confused.'

Illuminatus III. *A comment by Miss Portinari on the Illuminati, which is equally true of much occultism practised today.*

As we have shown in the previous chapter, magick has a complex and problematic history. The occult community has been dogged by the involvement of many misguided dubiously-motivated and ill-informed people. This situation has served to cloud magick with a fog different from, but as obscuring as that generated by the repressive patriarchal religions. Thus, the practice of occultism today has been fundamentally distorted by many of its supposed adherents.

35

Our own search for solutions led us to work with various groups and eventually form a circle of our own. Having experience of both sides of the esoteric fence made us aware of the flaws in the occult today, and this chapter will attempt to highlight these problems.

For the purposes of this chapter we consider that Wicca is identical with magick, an occult rather than religious path, and a method of ritual and symbolism. We acknowledge that Wicca is not the sole form through which occultism can be practised but it does seem to be true that today the majority of working magickians draw heavily on the balanced and open-ended format of Wicca.

The 'Craft' is the main way in which the general public, and other aspiring occultists including ourselves, first experience magick. The view of Wicca taken by the public, particularly in well educated urban areas, has changed dramatically over recent years leading to a far more tolerant and enlightened attitude to 'witches'. The simplistic idea of occultism as Satan worship is far less prevalent thanks to excellent publicity work on behalf of the Craft movement, mainly by Janet and Stewart Farrar, Nigel Bourne and Seldiy Bate.

Unfortunately the acceptability of terms such as 'witch' has allowed those with little or no understanding of magick but who exist on the fringes of occultism to freely employ this title. During the late 1970s and early 1980s when witchcraft enjoyed a steadily increasing popularity, many clairvoyants, tarot readers, astrologers and others adopted the 'witch' label. Whilst such techniques as tarot counselling are no less valid or important than ritual work, they do not alone constitute involvement in magick or the Craft. The psychic sciences are a necessary part of it but are not in themselves the sum total of magick.

Many prospective witches view the occult as a means of attaining material goals, or, misunderstanding magick's simplicity, believe it is a way to obtain power for egocentric aims. Other 'adepts' are fascinated with the glamour of magickal paraphernalia, both internal and external, thus becoming absorbed in obscure and often outmoded systems, which a close magickian friend of ours described as 'experts of detail and minions in magick'.

There are also today a minority of individuals who become obsessively engrossed in the idea of being a witch, magickian or similar; those who revel in the aura of mystery created by the Craft are often those chosen to be its representatives by the press. This is because they are considered both colourful characters and because it is easy to see how transparent they are when exposés are written. Such individuals are involved in Wicca for purely egotistic ends and have little or no magickal understanding. These people cause three things to occur, none of which are beneficial to the cause of occultism. They tend to perpetuate the psuedo-satanic hocus-pocus image of the Craft in the media. They become a focus for those genuinely interested in magick who contact them only to be either taken in or, if they see through these people, become discouraged from pursuing magick any further. Such individuals also often allow themselves to become involved with mentally unstable people for whom involvement in real magick, let alone another's fantasy world, could be disastrous.

Another problem today is that a high proportion of so-called occultists fail to grasp the basic tenets of magick. Concepts such as 'good and evil' and the 'right and left-hand paths' cause much confusion. As we have explained in the previous chapter, the Zoroastrian concept of good versus evil is entirely alien to magick (see p. 21) but this simple fact is often conveniently forgotten.

With misconceptions surrounding occult laws, it is perhaps not suprising that the nature of the deities has also been obscured. As we have said in the previous chapter on magick's early history, gods evolved as people progressed and changed. Initially, godforms were natural forces, not constructed abstract forms. It is probable that the Shaman instituted the concept of 'the gods' to humanise the occult energies. To paraphrase the Bible, 'Man created God in his own image'. All early belief systems were polytheistic, each godform represented part of the universal law of change.

The difficulty with understanding the nature of deities is that of comprehending relative levels of reality. There is the reality of physical existence, the reality of the astral realms, and that of other planes accessible to the magickian. The reality we ascribe to different states of being depends on the position of the observer. Kenneth Grant says in *Crowley and the Hidden God*, 'It should be abundantly clear to anyone with any experience of astral working and dream control that there is in truth nothing but a wakeful state of consciousness. We call the dream state such after dreaming has ceased; during actual dreaming no sense of illusion is experienced.' The gods act as repositories of power, they are inside us, as are all things in the universe. This is one of the fundamental doctrines of magick, that of the relationship between microcosm and macrocosm. Externalisation of godforms and the intellectual addition of symbols and names to these forces is simply an aid to their visualisation, providing keys which can be used to call upon these powers. Similarly, this describes the manner in which a being on the astral level can be said to be 'real' but the detail of its features is furnished by the individual's own imagination.

In the Craft, the identification of the gods with internal archetypes is dramatically brought home by the process of invocation. During the rite, the godforms become as one with the leaders of the ritual (see p. 108).

Even the nature of the 'traditional' god and goddess in Wicca has been corrupted. The esoteric knowledge of how a godforce is real has, in the main, been lost. Often this understanding has been replaced by the notion that the gods are only psychological pawns with no real power, or that the gods are religious absolutes that demand our worship.

The qualities and attributes, as well as reality of godforms, are also often incorrectly understood.

Deities were often symbolised by the use of planetary bodies (for example, the moon, the stars, the earth, etc.). It was understood that both masculine and feminine characteristics resided in these forces, irrespective of their symbolic gender (see p. 51 for more information on these terms). In general, godforms were divided into two complementary forms, symbolised by the two luminaries, the sun and moon. Both solar and lunar deities were worshipped. In modern times, the lunar goddess, chosen through Crowley's and Gardner's wish to re-awaken the oracular priestess (see previous chapter), has become synonymous with the female and the sun with the male in much of the Craft. Christianity served to identify the lunar energy with the concept of evil, therefore making the link with feminine power.

The image of the goddess has been robbed of much of its solar power, denying the 'passive' nature of the lunar god, and the inherent bisexuality which pervades all occult forms. Crowley's personal attitude to women, and to a lesser extent Gardner's, reflects his Victorian upbringing, and in spite of the matriarchal bias of the Craft, these prejudices pervade much of their work and ritual. Many of these early errors are still being repeated by today's 'witches'.

The Craft movement, in general, is at present lacking in honesty. Wicca has split into many different factions variously labelled Alexandrian, Gardnerian, Traditional, and others, which, despite the intergroup snobbery, employ virtually identical ritual structures.

Many occultists claim to have ancient traditions which in reality do not exist. They claim access to secret knowledge most of which is either imaginary or available in printed form. Many 'witches' use the Sabbats as social occasions, and are only interested in the superficial aspects of the occult.

'Neopagan' groups have grown up, instigated by those who wish to be involved in the occult but who are unwilling to investigate the existence of real power.

These groups have served to rob (in the public mind at least) the power from some very potent godforms. The neopagan groups claim that Wicca is identical to paganism. This is not so; a true pagan lived at one with the land; his rituals were observations of seasonal changes connected to the hunting and the gathering of food (see pp. 16–18) and so he had no use for many of the elements that make up Gardner/Crowley Wicca, or its modern 'pagan' relations.

The secretive and rigidly hierarchial nature of the early covens has brought about a situation in which only fragmented magickal knowledge has been passed on. Few groups operate any type of training system, and numerous problems have emerged in direct relation to this lack of training. Early in the Craft's history many of the Gardnerian groups closed their doors so that other individuals in search of magickal knowledge were only able to obtain a fragment of the ritual/magickal material available pertaining to Wicca. In this way, ignorant occultists have bred others of their kind. A further problem is that those who discover Wicca can, by the scarcity of information, be convinced that there really are great spell books and fantastic rites which hold the keys to power. One of the great initiations happens when the seeker understands that Craft rituals are only badly written, jumbled texts and, as the Charge says, '. . . if that which thou seekest thou findest not within thee thou wilt never find it without thee.'

The positive side to this is that, as the seeker looks for the hidden mysteries in books, so when he or she discovers that the secrets are internal, they will have either gathered a wealth of occult information in the search, or will have left magick in favour of a less demanding path.

More difficulties develop when uncommited individuals enter the training system of a reputable group and leave without completing their tuition.

Striving for 'traditional' roots to excuse ineptitude, many groups cling to the simplistic material produced by Gardner, Crowley, and Valiente, at Wicca's birth.

The Wiccan *Book of Shadows*, which was originally intended as a ritual framework not a litany (its correct use is demonstrated by the Wiccan rites produced by Janet and Stewart Farrar), is often adhered to verbatim although it offers little in practical knowledge. It is obvious that a priest or priestess without occult or life experience cannot teach or assist others if their only knowledge is from this source, particularly as the *Book of Shadows* has undergone numerous rewrites and miscopies.

Inadequacies in today's groups are often compensated for, at least on a surface level, by the invention of magickal genealogy. These mythical traditions produce an artificial litany and line of heredity to compensate for their lack of information. Petty-minded rules operate in some groups, not designed for necessary discipline but to give the 'leaders' power born of fear, and to restrict questioning by the group members.

There are those who are sincere occultists who fail objectively to analyse the system they are using. They seem content to use the incomplete and garbled present-day Wiccan ritual and fail to ask themselves how it can be improved. In groups lacking knowledge their ritual reflects this by the way it lacks physical participation. We acknowledge that some rituals do not necessitate much physical movement but in a group the will to 'get up and do' is vital.

The initiatory system, designed at first to confer power and in subsequent ritual to confer rank and authority based on experience, has also been debased. Today it is often used to create elitism amongst occultists, producing a transparent and ironic pseudo-meritocracy. Initiation proper occurs internally; it is a continual process of change and development. It is true that power, or the beginnings of it, can be transmitted through a physical rite of initiation but the idea of the Craft mysteries being 'gloriously revealed' to the initiate is completely false. Understanding is only gained through hard work.

In many groups working a three-tiered, or three-degree

system of initiation, it is often given without due consideration for the individual's motivation and level of understanding. Honest commitment cannot be made in ignorance.

The second-degree Wiccan initiation was intended to mark the individual's ability to work magickally with minimum supervision from the High Priestess. A couple wishing to 'hive off' (or begin a new coven) could do so whilst maintaining contact with the mother coven. The third degree, involving the use of the Great Rite (sex magic), was a ritual to be worked by an existing magickal partnership to enable the partners to obtain independence and greater power. The Great Rite has, particularly over the last few years, enjoyed a somewhat unfortunate history. The sexual aspect has resulted in abuse through ignorance and deliberate deception. Sex magick presents problems because of the tremendously potent and profound energy released by this formula. Misuse of sex magick is quite literally playing with fire; unless correctly directed its creativity can be warped into a downward spiral of pointless destruction.

In explaining the misuse of the third degree, there are groups with the puritanical notion that the occult should not involve sexuality. Many of the superficial neopagan groups have adopted an asexual goddess who is an ornament rather than an agent of power, creating what one occultist has described as 'Jehovah in drag'.

Whilst paying lip service to the female principle, they are by their own actions weakening (if momentarily) the astral essence of the goddess.

The ritual of 'Drawing Down the Moon' commonly used as an invocation has unfortunately consolidated the above misconception. The passive lunar force is invoked into the High Priestess during the opening of most ritual circles. Often without considering its effects or propriety, she is then expected to continue her active role of leading the rite and act as the cohesive leader of the group. In the majority of groups, no equivalent solar force is invoked and the psychological imbalance can create real problems for the priest and priestess.

Whilst maintaining a contradictory role, the priestess is expected to create a balanced force in herself and her coven; her priest is expected to support her and offer his power. Imagine the reaction of the emasculated priest who has no function to fulfil but to act as an impotent consort to the goddess, and indeed how can the priestess accept power from a priest who has none? This is the antithesis of male dominated Christianity and can be just as damaging.

Lunar workings are considered safe but the power evoked is insidious (the magickal equivalent of 'what you don't see can't hurt you). In classical correspondence the moon is the ruler of the astral plane, and those habitually working with such a current risk becoming absorbed in the astral and losing touch with physical (earth) reality. As A.C. Highfield states in the occult magazine, *Formaos*, 'It is particularly important in pathworking to clearly delineate between 'inner' and 'outer' experiences, to avoid, in esoteric language "confusing one's planes".'

Over the past twenty years, the Craft has incorporated other mythical genealogies diversifying from Gardner's original Greek mythology. Problems arise when research into these systems is incomplete and when selective use of other mythos structures degenerates into an occult magpie fixation.

Many individuals have been so concerned with the introduction of other cultures that the resultant rituals become a conglomeration of juxtaposed godforms. In misunderstanding the purpose of the deities the whole direction of the rite may be changed. Godforms contain an internal power which, even if successfully invoked in ignorance, will manifest in its true form. On a more mundane level this trend has been demonstrated by the way that modern marriages are often blessed in numerous ceremonies, Wiccan, Hindu, Buddhist, and so on.

This tendency is mirrored in the manner that many children are brought up by parents involved in the occult. In recent years, the first of the truly hereditary witches are reaching an age when they should be understanding the ethics and principles of their Wiccan parents.

It is to be hoped that from these children, new truth and understanding will grow. However, many of this generation are not only unaware of the nature of their parents' beliefs but in some cases have been given a deliberate bias in opposite directions. Whilst not advocating brain washing, or the assumption that any individual whatever age should accept the beliefs of its parents, the tolerance, awareness, respect and added insight that parents involved in the occult should have developed, can only be beneficial to a child. Freedom of thought and action are essential to the occultist, though many seem to hold these values in theory rather than in practice. Whilst no belief, occult or otherwise, should be forced on a child, the essence of the parents' beliefs should be made available to the child, and explained in a way befitting his or her level of understanding. Wiccan parents should remain open about what they think, and should try to dispel the disruptive secrecy that has surrounded magick for so long. It is also a valid point that in a post-Christian society, increasing numbers of children are encountering different religious forms, often involving the archetype of the goddess, such as Hinduism, for example.

If children are not given freedom of choice or are not allowed to maintain an open-minded attitude, then there is no hope either for the future of magick or society at large.

The problems outlined above grow from, in principle, lack of commitment both to the concept of magick as ritual, and magick as a philosophy of everyday life. From a positive point of view, many aspects of the occult are increasingly accepted: astrology, complementary medicine, hypnosis, etc., once considered as being the practices of cranks, are now more integrated into today's society.

Finally, it must be said that this corruption is happening through all sections of society, and not just within the occult world. It is the natural precursor of the new Aeon, and it is the job of the occultist to change and develop in awareness first, so that we may aid the correct manifestation of the coming age.

CHAPTER 3
PRIMITIVE POWER

'When a man decides to do something, he must go all the way . . . but he must take responsibility for what he does. No matter what he does, he must know first why he is doing it, and then he must proceed with his actions without having doubts or remorse about them.'
The Teachings of Don Juan

In this chapter we will describe the areas of magick that we have retained within our own magickal form that we call Serket, together with the other influences that have been incorporated into this current. More importantly we wish to explain the meanings and concepts behind ideas like 'the gods', and 'karma', as they are used in occultism.

A god or goddess is, as we have explained in Chapter 1, based on an archetypal form. This is not to say that the gods are simply personal expressions of the human mind. Occult theory states that a force, such as the Egyptian deity, Horus, for example, exists on many levels. In its simplest form this god is vitalised by those people working with, or worshipping it. At a more profound level the energy 'Horus' is animated because it is an expression of a certain wavelength of energy within the universe. In the same way, the colour 'red' in the visible spectrum is real. We can see it, it affects humans on a bio-chemical, psychological and occult basis. Even if we were unable to experience red light waves or we did not consider them to be 'real' they would still exist. The principle of the relationship between microcosm and macrocosm shows that all the universe is a display of the working of our higher or greater self, and that if we gain the keys the higher self can be linked directly to the individual.

In the words of the ancient Egyptian initiate, 'There is no part of me which is not of the Gods.' In the same way radio waves are 'real' but cannot be used by the person unless the correct key (i.e. a radio receiver) is employed. It is necessary to point out that the higher self pervades all, and as such it is common to each individual. At this level, concepts such as 'group', 'real' and 'personal' cease to have any meaning, to use the Qabalistic analogy, 'All is One and One is All.'

In a ritual it is the godform that acts as the radio receiver. The image of Horus contains keys that can allow this link between the macro and microcosm to occur. It is often simpler for the human intellect to work with Horus than an abstract idea, such as that of the higher self. In Serket, we have retained the symbol of the Circle for just this reason. The human mind finds the concept of an infinite universe a difficult one to comprehend (except in ecstatic states) so the magick circle serves both to contain the magickal energy raised and to define the perimeters of the magickian's universe. For the duration of the rite the adept is creating a cosmos in which he or she is in command. Again to help the occultist, the circle is divided into Dark and Light, the basic unit of polarity. Then it is divided into the elements, Fire, Air, Water, Earth, and then if necessary into smaller units: the seven planets, the spheres on the Tree of Life, numerology, and others. In this way the abstract of 'the universe' is made personal to the occultist. The use of gods and goddesses helps to personalise energy, and assists the magickian in selecting logically appropriate images, scents, actions, and so on, which will appeal to the 'instinctive' higher self. This division can be expressed in terms of the three-fold diagram in Figure 1 on page 48.

The mind can be understood as being split into three levels. These are not actual areas of division but are simply aids in explanation, a useful means of classification. It is

47

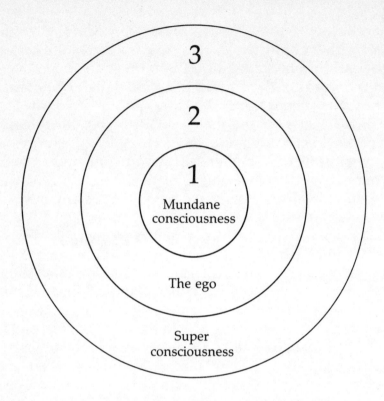

Figure 1. Three-fold model of consciousness

important to point out that in this context the mind is not identical with the brain. The mind is an energy which transcends the body, in the same way that the function of memory does not have a governing centre within the physical brain structure. The mind interacts with the brain, which in turn interacts with the body. In a similar fashion the mind itself is based on a three-tiered matrix.

The outer circle represents the subconscious, but not merely as the habitation of desires and memory. This area, labelled 'superconscious', is identical to spirit, the higher self, the macrocosm. It is the 'pattern', the all pervading field of energy that flows throughout all levels of reality. This part of the mind communicates using the language of symbols, dramatic images and archetypes. The innermost or smallest circle represents everyday consciousness. This is the aspect of mind which deals with mundane matters, its method of communication is words and symbols, such as formed by the alphabet. The link between these levels of the mind is the ego. The ego is able to deal in both words and symbols, and is the area between these wavelengths of being. In unawakened people the ego acts as an uncontrolled guardian.

Information flowing from the superconscious is repressed because the individual's ego is not willing to accept the information. Even in states when the links between minds one and three are closer, during dreaming, for example, the ego still colours the information, creating a complex and perhaps nonsensical experience. This 'stained glass effect' of the mundane ego is negated by the magickian who can for a time experience a 'voluntary insanity' (total knowledge of all that is is the most extreme form of madness!) by touching minds one and three and then closing down when the work is complete. The ego, in the guise of the archetypal magickal force, a god, an angel, etc., is deliberately manipulated. Thus, even the gods must come under the direction of the True Will.

Each godform (for example one of the seven major planetary powers) is a key which exists is many ways, allowing the linking of the micro and macrocosm, as depicted in Figure 2.

The 'pattern' to which the gods are mediators is the sea of possibilities called the universal mind. It is the gateway to all power and all knowledge, past, present and future. As such it is the Chaos of modern magick and the Akashic record which already knows what events will occur, as it has foreknowledge of the actions of free will. The god/goddess archytypes used to gain access to this reservoir of power operate at different levels depending on the intensity and depth of symbolism within any given godform. It is interesting to note that many forms now considered deities were originally people. Deities such as Maraduk, Odin, and

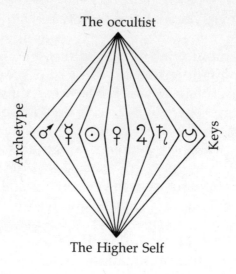

Figure 2. Keys to linking microcosm and macrocosm

Osiris, all have part of their roots in historical kings or heroes. The same deification has occured in more recent times with other dramatic personalities, notably Robin Hood, King Arthur (both of whom are arguably archetypes in their own right), Hitler, and Aleister Crowley.

This process of deification has been continued in Christianity by the process of canonisation, and even by some members of the Craft movement with the reverence payed to many of the characters who have been involved in Wicca. Many of these gods were the ancient equivalent of modern algebraic expressions used to illustrate certain ideas. Osiris represented man, or the initiate; Christ, in a non-historic sense, represented the Son of the Sun, Tiphereth in the Qabalah. It is strange to find many thousands of years on people actively worshipping an image which was originally intended as an allegorical symbol!

The godform chosen for a specific ritual should operate according to archetypal rules. Different deities will access different forces from the macrocosm in the same way that different lenses or crystals can refract a given wavelength of light from the spectrum. Godforces such as Ares, Babalon, or Tu, will evoke the fiery positive areas of the macrocosm and allow communication with these levels of the self.

The science of correspondences, another essential part of magick, serves to group energies within the higher self into classes which are labelled using the seven planets, or perhaps the Major Arcana of the tarot, and so on.

The more clearly an archetype is portrayed, the more potent the results. The only qualification on which to base the use of a deity should be its effectiveness in stimulating the cosmic and personal levels in the magickian. In Serket, we have simply used the terms 'the god' and 'the goddess' as these phrases do not restrict that energy to any particular cultural or mythical type. Early archetypes and 'titles' help the magickian to select the energy necessary, together with the concept of 'aspects', expressed as the four phases of the sun or the moon. Godforms are referred to as 'Lord of Fallen Summer', 'Dark Serpent', 'Hag Goddess', and in this way extraneous imagery is avoided. If a single goddess image was habitually used, Diana, for example, then the group could become limited to that form, and oracular work for instance will tend to be consistently clothed in Greco–Roman imagery, even when this is undesirable. On the occasions that we have digressed from this method we have used either a very specific godform or a system of deities which still express the necessary archetypal force invoked. This is true of the early Egyptian mythos to which our own group are all attuned in some way. Ultimately, whatever name is used it is the intent and visualisation held by the group that must be complete and accurate in order for the correct energy to be invoked.

Using 'primitive' godforms, such as totemic, atavistic energies, can result in access to deep levels of the higher self. Also, 'modern' forms based on early forces, such as Mat-ion, Yog Sothoth, Cthulu, can access those same profound levels of power. This magick is identical to the work of activating the 'Elder Gods', a term explained in the fiction of H.P. Lovecraft and Kenneth Grant's *Typhonian Trilogy*, as these powers are identical to the forces of our future selves.

Another part of early tribal magiculture we have retained in Serket is that of the observance of the seasons. The union of the macrocosm and the microcosm is aided when the magickian is in touch with the tides of the moon, the seasons, the planets, and through them the self. Seasonal rites can harness potent magical cycles in the year and also act as dramatic aids in self-analysis.

All systems and mythological forms contain elements of truth. In evolving our rites we have researched many cultures and formulated a system which is essentially common to all mythologies and can be seen to be internally consistent.

Serket acknowledges the concept of karma as this is a universal law and not an idea that can be either accepted or rejected. Many individuals and groups misunderstand the Laws of Karma. Some believe karma to be a divine force which rewards good deeds and punishes evil. Karma is not fatalistic nor is it universal fair play. Karma is simply the law of cause and effect: any energy emitted from a point ultimately returns and affects the point that first started the chain of events. The universe's job is to maintain balance, not to act as a moralistic angel of retribution. Once the magickian makes the commitment to the True Will then he or she becomes the centre of their universe. The occultist's only moral code is that expressed by the Book of The Law, 'Do what thou wilt shall be the whole of the Law', and 'Love is the law; Love under Will.' This means that all responsibility falls on the magickian's shoulders, and that there is no god or devil to blame for any failure to follow the course of the True Will. All emotions, even love, must lie under the constant direction of the Will. The concept of 'Love under

Will' is explained by W. Gray in relation to the mystery of the ankh-shaped knot of Isis, 'To control Venus, the secret of her Zona, or girdle, had to be known. It was tied with a special knot, and its pattern hid the secret.

Once this was mastered, Love came under control of Will, for the knot could be fastened or unfastened according to the initiate's intention.' The acceptance of this law is the ultimate test of magickal courage. When The Oath (however it is taken) to the Great Work (True Will) is made then the occultist will find that what he or she would like or wants becomes unimportant. If the commitment is made then it must be carried through and the oath to the Great Work should never be taken lightly.

Another universal law is that of reincarnation. Many oriental cultures explain this process in terms of transmigration, that is to say incarnation from, for example, an insect, to animal, to human form. Often this explanation is simply used as a graphic image to demonstrate the process but some groups take this image literally. Reincarnation is simply the law of evolution as applied to other levels of reality, and literal transmigration is demonstrably false. This view regards species other than human beings as states held only by unevolved souls, or those of people who have committed sins while in human form. Again this philosophy can be traced to Zoroaster, and robs animals of their dignity as parts of a whole eco-system, no better or worse than mankind. It would be more correct to say that a person's consciousness may incarnate on a physical level, an astral level and so forth, in a similar way to the druidic heliocentric theory which again on a surface level appears to be transmigratory. It is more accurate to say that each individual exists on all levels. There is not so much a change of state, it is more that one becomes aware that one is already at that state. In Tantra, the serpent force of kundalini is not so much raised as the individual becomes aware of kundalini's existence and action within a rite.

We have retained the basic framework of Wicca, keeping

the roles of High Priest and High Priestess, and much of the Craft's basic structure. We still use parts of Wiccan material, The Charge, the form of casting the Circle, etc., simply because of their beauty and power. Above all we would like to point out that Serket is not an ancient tradition. Whilst its fundamental principles are common to all occultism, much of its structure is a result of research into and practical experience of magickal forms and the most effective symbolism to use in a ritualistic situation. Serket also incorporates elements drawn from Tantra, Thelema, and other esoteric paths.

The work of Aleister Crowley has provided a useful springboard from which large areas of Serket's nature have evolved. This system was not clinically fashioned but grew slowly from the union of our complementary views, experience, knowledge and ideals. Crowley adopted many tantric practices and attempted, with a fair degree of success, to apply them to the Western magickal system. Much of the work by Crowley was intellectual or oracular and was never successfully applied in rituals. The Thelemic oracular texts, such as *Liber AL*, have been of much use to occultists, including ourselves, as has much of his theoretical work. Crowley had a very unbalanced personality as a man, and an unhealthy attitude to sexuality and women. His priestesses were often prostitutes rather than Whores in the magickal sense of the term (see Chapter 4). Despite this, Crowley's influence on the Craft and the occult world of today has been marked and can, if properly understood, be beneficial.

The elements that form the basis of Wiccan paraphernalia also remain. That is to say the use of the elemental weapons (ascribing the sword to Fire and the wand to Air in general work). We continue to use the Qabalah as both a 'filing system' for magickal correspondences, and also in an extended format for magickal work at both practical and theoretical levels. Other influences have permeated the fabric of the Serket system such as the work of Austin Osman Spare, as well as information gleaned from group pathworkings, regressions and oracular texts.

The next chapter will explain how sexuality is the principle key to all occultism, and how polarity works as the most potent key to the reservoir of the higher self.

CHAPTER 4
SECRETS OF SEXUALITY

'The Goddess resides in all women and the Lord within all men.'
Jvalauali Vajramala

Magick is based on the interaction of complementary elements; the foundation of all occult systems is this law of polarity. The function of polarity is dramatically expressed by the use of 'sex magick' in many cultures as the most obvious exhibition of complementary forces at work.

Early goddess orientated cultures did not have the restrictive sexual taboos that abound in modern society and often the energy of the sexual act was directed to a magickal aim. Originally, sex magick was directly related to physical fertility, both in crops, animals and within the tribe itself. Many of the orgiastic rites held in these cultures were acts of sympathetic magick and also provided the group with a positive way to release emotional tension. The sexual energy generated by these rites was directed by the Shaman to a magickal end. Unfortunately, as society evolved sexual taboos, these orgiastic rituals became more a release of repressed sexual elements and frustrations. In later cultures much of this emotional release emerged in the form of violence rather than positive creation. This is the probable origin of the sex equals violence equation, which is still sadly common in our society. This change was illustrated by the slow debasement of such rites as those of Bacchus and of Inanna.

The essence of the Craft grew from the fertility cult of the womb but the aim of magick today should be concerned with the fertility of the mind. On the subject of physical fertility, many misunderstandings about the role of the goddess have led to the belief that the High Priestess of a group should retire when she is no longer physically fertile. This rule would exclude priestesses who are still technically fertile but using some method of contraception.

It is doubtful that any woman, priestess or otherwise, would relish the prospect of semi-permanent pregnancy. Pregnancy naturally causes the woman to introvert and internalise her energies making it difficult for a priestess to actively lead a ritual under these circumstances. This belief exaggerates the importance of physical fertility, and displays an ignorance of the functions of the wise or active dark goddess. This misconception may have grown from the practice of creating 'magickal children'. These children have been interpreted as physical rather than mental offspring. Magickal children can be ideas, oracular texts, or indeed any form of magick that manifests either at an inspirational or physical level.

Just as sex is part of a balanced life, so in a magickal context sex is important but should not devolve into an obsession. All occult systems involve sexual polarity and to remove the sexual element from Wicca is to castrate the goddess and the god.

All rituals use polarity in the same way as sex magick but this can be expressed symbolically, such as in the use of the athame and the chalice in the symbolic Great Rite. Janet and Stewart Farrar explain this in their book *Eight Sabbats for Witches*, 'The "actual" Great Rite is sex magic while the symbolic Great Rite is the magic of gender.' The symbolic Great Rite can be just as powerful as the physical Great Rite, the difference being in the qualities of the energies raised.

Much of the terminology and symbolism of sex magick used in the West today has been synthesised from the cult of Tantra. Whilst the Earth Mother megalithic culture was active in Europe, in Southern India the first Tantric texts were being written. The early emergence of written information allowed Tantra to spread rapidly and become one of the earliest influences on other magicultures, notably those of Sumeria and Egypt. Tantra incorporates various magickal and yogic practices: control of breathing, yoga, the use of yantra and mantra (symbolic magick and chanting respectively) and sexual rites. The role of the priest and priestess in Tantra is symbolised by the interaction of Shiva and Shakti, the Tantric equivalent terms for the Craft god and goddess.

The use of sex magick is often termed 'left-hand path'. This distinction refers to the way that Tantra uses the feminine principle. Unlike later Hinduism, Tantra is free of a caste system in which women are seen as inferior. Tantra emphasises the goddess as the source of life, the creatorix and director of power. Tantra teaches that occult insight is not derived from rejecting the material world, as does the ascetic, but by participating and using matter as an aid to understanding. Unlike patriarchal faiths, Tantra teaches that matter is as holy as spirit; therefore tantriks use wine, drugs, and sexual activities, as well as yogic exercises, in order to achieve enlightenment.

It must be understood that Tantra is not simply an excuse for excess in the mundane sense of the word. The usage of Tantric practices should be carefully controlled and the path of Tantra should only be used by those with a high degree of magickal understanding. All the rites of Tantra are performed in honour of the goddess and the god (higher self) not for self gratification in the egotistical sense. In Crowley's *The Book of the Law* this same concept is expressed, '. . . dress ye all in fine apparel; eat rich foods and drink sweet wines and wines that foam! Also, take your fill and will of love as ye will, when, where and with whom ye will! But always unto me.'

A variety of techniques and practices are used by the devotees of Tantra. For example, the practice of 'Karezza' in which the partners raise energy by delaying the physical event of orgasm for the maximum amount of magickal power. The female actively directs the ritual whilst the male takes the role of the 'passive' lunar god. At the moment of most tension, orgasm is allowed to occur and the magickal force released is directed to a specific, predetermined aim. Tantric practices also include the generation of oracular states in consciousness usually, though not exclusively, in the priestess.

The majority of Tantric practices are designed to stimulate the force of kundalini, which is symbolised as a serpent coiled three and a half times round the base of the spine. The energy channelled by this force can be used for diverse types of magickal workings by allowing it to stimulate different chakras. It is likely that the Tantric element was instilled into the Craft by Aleister Crowley, whose understanding of the subject was intellectually if not emotionally complete. To effectively understand and use Tantra one must understand the true role and nature of Woman.

Tantric practices were not exclusive to Asian culture and were practised in many other countries, including China, Egypt, and Sumeria. As an example, in Cyprus each suitable woman spent a period of time in the temple learning and performing the duties of a priestess, before marriage. These devotees of Aphrodite were considered honoured because they were the representatives of the goddess whose first sexual union would be with a man who represented the god. Anyone could buy the favours of these women (although it is probable that priests from other temples often played this role) but only once and for any sum of money (afterwards the money was kept as a talisman).

Temple prostitution was a form of first initiation into the secrets of sexuality. After such a union the women were still considered 'virgin' and any children born as a result were said to be 'born of a virgin'. In this respect it is interesting to note the use of the word virgin in the Bible with respect to Mary.

The importance of sexual polarity provides the key to the

understanding of occultism. There are three physiological events that are the origin of magick's 'blood' mysteries. In Tantra, the Shakti (goddess) represents the elements of Fire and blood, the physical manifestation of which holds the secret of women's mysteries. As Kenneth Grant explains in *The Typhonian Trilogy*, the word secret has its roots in the word secretion. Blood is life, and natural loss of blood is an offering of power. These three blood mysteries are: the blood of hymen rupture (in many ways identical to the blood of a woman's first period as both these events are true initiations commencing new phases in the woman's life), the blood of menstruation, and the blood of childbirth. These times were magickally significant, symbolising three aspects of the goddess.

At the time of a girl's first period she would withdraw from the rest of society for a time of seclusion accompanied by various rituals, not because she was considered unclean but out of consideration for the woman. After experiencing her first period it seems likely that the Shaman of the tribe acted as sexual initiator to the young female, and indeed to the adolescent male, introducing them to the finer points of sexuality. Hymen rupture, often synonymous with first menstruation, became a rite of passage into adulthood. Later, hymen rupture became more associated with a male conquering a woman and removing her 'purity'. He was in some ways supposed to degrade her (as in the tradition of hanging out the bridal sheet covered with her maiden blood) rather than symbolically demonstrate her sexual maturity.

Women then, as now, were evidently more sensitive and withdrawn around the time of their period but instead of being expected to function as 'normal' were allowed to internalise and use their magickal senses. The early cultures would set aside a hut or building for the menstruating or premenstruating women to withdraw into. Under the guidance of an older woman or priestess, they would be instructed in the subjects of sex, religion and tribal lore. It is accepted magickally that a woman is more likely to be oracular and clairvoyant at this, rather than other times in her cycle. Many standard laboratory tests have confirmed this esoteric law. Women engaged in ESP tests have shown significantly more 'hits' around this time in their cycle, particularly if the menstrual cycle coincides with significant points in the lunar rhythm. However, she is in a mundane way more likely to be irritable, emotional and clumsy.

As men became more afraid of magick, this powerful time became surrounded by taboos, which to some extent we still suffer from today. Later, fear became disgust, particularly in cultures so far removed from biological reality that blood was no longer observed. Sexuality and the blood associated with aspects of sex were rejected as being offensive or dirty and this feeling was extended to the woman herself. Rituals designed to sanctify menstruation became rituals to instil shame in the woman. It was considered that a woman's virginity was renewed after a period; the ritual bath of Judaism and Islam, originally instituted to symbolise this rebirth, took on the aspect of a ceremony of purification.

In a survivalist society where paternity was not encompassed, the giving forth of blood was observed with awe. Women would have spent a large proportion of their lives pregnant and periods would be comparatively rare. The term 'blood sacrifice' was originally applied to menstrual blood and not to animal or human sacrifice. Sinead Sulce Grian in her book *Brighde's Fire* suggests that these later offerings were the poor attempt of patriarchy to mimic the deathless sacrifice of blood by woman.

Blood issuing from the womb represents the flow of power and life from the goddess. This imagery has permeated all facets of the left-hand path: from the flooding of the Nile and the deposition of red clay to a libation poured from the chalice in a Wiccan ritual, the symbolism is obvious. As the awe and power instilled by magick turned to fear, society's sacrifices became bloody slaughterings.

Once the reproductive cycle was understood, menstruation took on a different significance. It showed that the woman was not pregnant and therefore had failed to fulfil her role in a patrilinear society of providing her husband with an heir. It began to be associated with barrenness.

The third blood mystery is that of the blood of childbirth. This emission vividly demonstrated the link between blood and life. Magickly, pregnancy internalises the woman's energy but it serves to give her (and her partner if any) one of the longest and most difficult initiations, that of successfully bringing up a child. Like the previously mentioned mysteries, the sanctity of 'birth blood' too became degraded. The original evolutionary importance of womb fertility degenerated into a desire for progeny, particularly male progeny. Pregnancy deteriorated into a way of subduing and controlling the woman in the same way as she became dominated by the sex act itself.

Just as the moon has three visible faces, waxing, full and waning, but also has a fourth that is invisible at the new moon, there is also a hidden or dark face corresponding to the fourth blood mystery. This mystery is that of the hag goddess who does not give forth blood, as too the village wise woman or tribal matriarch. In mythology, she is Tiamat, Rhiannon, Kali, and symbolises the crone aspect of the goddess. Her age made her the living representative of all faces of the goddess: she had experienced childhood, menstruation, motherhood, and seen around her the evidence of death and regeneration.

She was wise because she had survived so long and her counsel was valued because of her wealth of experience. In terms of our life expectancy, an old woman of an early tribe could have been any age from thirty onwards, although fertility may have commenced at about nine or ten. Her age refers to her aspect not her number of years, as many ballads and folk legends show how she can change aspects at will from youth to age and back. The hag queen was the leader of the Tantrik Karezza rite in her Indian form of Kali who dances on the 'corpse' of her lover Shiva, the passive

62

principal of the God. The hidden face of the goddess also refers to the emission of the secretion that is not red, namely vaginal lubricant. The importance of this secret should be apparent to anyone who has studied Tantra or the informative if rather obscure works of Kenneth Grant.

In a patriarchal society where women's mysteries are seldom taught, the importance of this fourth or 'hidden face' is lost even to the majority of Wiccans; this means they fail to understand such goddess forms as those listed above. Hecate is one such example as a goddess of death but also of fertility, the blood mysteries, and therefore of life itself.

Society reflects on a material level prejudices which have their roots in superstitions. The partnership of the youthful 'passive' god and the wise, dark goddess is mistrusted in the same way that in patriarchy the relationship between an older man and young woman is accepted whilst the reverse situation is frowned on out of superstitious fear.

In earlier chapters we have described the prevalent attribution of male to solar, and female to lunar currents. We hope here to show how this simplistic division is based on some fundamental magickal errors. In cultures following that of the megalithic culture, for example Celtic/Druidic complexes, Cerridwen, and other deities of her ilk, was the solar goddess containing all four aspects of the feminine archetype. Cerridwen represents the whole of the goddess archetype. In the same way, many major goddesses contain all aspects. For instance, Ishtar is not one particular female deity, in fact her name means simply 'goddess'. Isis simply means 'nature', and was an overall form comprising various aspects, Isis-Sept, Nu-Isis, etc. These overall forms do not have particular personalities like goddesses of specific aspects. Cerridwen directed the solar wheel through the sky in a coracle or ark, the shape of an upturned crescent. The shape of this boat has lead to the mistaken belief that Cerridwen was a lunar deity.

Others mistakenly hold the belief (historians and archaeologists included) that pre-Christian godforms were religious absolutes. Study of mythology and magick shows the falsehood of this theory.

Cerridwen was still seen as being subject to the laws of creation, which were neither male nor female; she was an intermediary to the cosmic forces but not herself an omnipotent ruler. Similarly in Greek culture, the three-pointed crescent of Hecate was not a lunar symbol, it was the trident of flames shown in the symbolism of the Hebrew letter Shin, 'the triple tongue of the fire snake'. Further confusion arose from the term 'Son of the sun', applied to the light aspect of the god force. The sun was not male but was the solar goddess. Her offspring is the 'crowned and conquering child'; this was her son and her lover who was to be her sacrifice. The solar goddess is the archetype of the Whore (in the sense of Crowley's Babalon), Virgin, Hag and Mother, all in one. Once patriarchy identified the sun with the god force, the lunar god was rejected and labelled submissive, effeminate and homosexual. Christianity at first identified the Christ with 'the Son of the sun' but later confused this with the concept that he was a solar deity.

The lunar god (identical to such deities as Set, Shiva and Shaitan) became degraded in Christianity into the adversary of the anti-female solar god — Satan. The lunar god was rejected because he contained what patriarchy feared: feminine (but not necessarily female) characteristics, and was for this reason to be distrusted. He was ritually passive, the chaos of magickal power directed by the goddess (usually in her Hag or Whore aspect), the male participant in Karezza, and many other sex magick formulae. The goddess harnesses his power, 'Babalon bridles the Beast', as Crowley put it. The lunar god was often symbolised in an atavistic form. It is this union between the Beast (lunar god) and Woman (solar goddess) that is the basis of many major cults: the goat and woman in mediaeval witchcraft, the swan and Leda in Greek mythology, the Dove and the Virgin Mary in Christianity.

Often these magickal matings resulted in progeny who

were metaphors for occult forces or currents. Loki and Angrboda in Norse myth spawned Fenris the Great Wolf, Jormungand the serpent and the goddess Hel.

The goddess is the Whore in the sense that she is the 'desire of the heart of man', the archetypal lover of the male psyche. She is the temple prostitute of the unconscious. The symbolism of the Whore is that of the chalice full of wine or blood, an image common in all occult paths (Christianity, Thelema, African beliefs, etc.). In magickal terms this is another reference to Tantra. The blood is the raw power of the priest (as the Beast or Lunar God), symbolically his semen which is absorbed into the chalice (vagina) of the priestess. The liquid is not itself altered but it conforms to the shape of the vessel it is within. The Whore controls the force of the priest, absorbing his energy into herself and giving form to his power. Thus the magickal energy of the rite, be it sexual or not, is moulded into reality.

All aspects of myth relate to psycho-sexual currents of energy. The legend of the dying god (the son/lover of the goddess) touches on a fundamental attribute of the self. During the sexual act, the male desires to be so deeply within the female, both on a physical, emotional and possibly magickal level, that he can fertilise her with his own seed so that he may be reborn and be her child. The female desires the male to fertilise her and for her lover to 'become her child'.

In saying this we must stress two points. Firstly, this desire is, for the most part, active only at a subconscious level. Secondly, the term 'fertilise' has many different implications depending on what level the fertilisation takes place. In this way the male desires to 'die' within the woman in order that he may be reborn.

This motif is expressed in the symbol of the phoenix and the Australian aboriginal saying, 'The vagina is very hot, it is fire and each time the penis goes in, it dies.'

Just as the goddess contains all masculine and feminine aspects so does the god force. The balance of these powers can be shown by the representation of the god as twins, as in Set and Horus from Egyptian mythology. Set and Horus symbolise the feminine and masculine forms of the godforce thus serving to illustrate the point that the ascribed gender of a deity is no sure guide to its nature or occult function. The interaction of the god and goddess is also depicted in many ways as mother and son, or brother and sister, as in the Basque witch culture where Lucifer is the lunar god and Aradia the solar goddess who are both offspring of Diana.

Dynamic balance is important; just as in ancient times the priestesses served the god force and the priests the goddess, in the same way occultism assigns the chalice to the priest and the sword to the priestess. This network of interlinking polarity is common to deities, as it must be to the magickian whose aim it is to be at one with them.

CHAPTER 5

MAGICKAL RELATIONSHIPS

'The Fire Snake is the "and" in 'Yin and Yang.'
Gary Kirkby

Whilst magickal laws remain constant, their expression changes with regard to the society they manifest through. The following chapter explores the role of sexuality in magick at an individual and group, rather than archetypal level. The magickian must understand his or her own sexuality in order to understand magick. In discussing magickal sexuality, terms such as masculine/feminine and male/female must be clarified. The first two terms are descriptions of characteristics, while the second two refer to physical gender. The goddess whilst being symbolised by a woman has both masculine and feminine traits. Feminine characteristics, such as intuition, passivity and emotion, are common in both genders. Magick explains that the female is more active on the astral plane and less active on the physical; the reverse of this is true of the male. Whilst the physical body is either male or female, the developed psyche of any individual is, like the archetype of the tribal Shaman, androgenous. In this way, every magickian must be bisexual.

Magickal bisexuality need not be expressed in directly sexual terms, in either homosexual or heterosexual relationships, but the occultist should be aware that both energies of the psyche should be able to manifest through the physical body. The conscious growth of this magickal androgeny has been mentioned by many occult writers. Aleister Crowley wrote, 'Observe for yourselves . . . the strange modifications of the reproductive instinct with the tendency to become bisexual or epicene.' Whether an individual is physically homosexual, heterosexual, or bisexual is immaterial as long as the person feels genuinely comfortable with their own sexuality. The main criterion is that the androgenous self can fully manifest in the individual. Physical gender is important, and its rejection is just as restricting as ignoring the androgeny of the self. In a ritual, an exclusively homosexual male could not assume the role and title of priestess for just this reason. In magick the formula of reversal is a valid technique but reversal of physical gender roles has more egocentric than occult implications. The formula of reversal, in its simplest form, states that most magickal energy can be generated when as many crosses of subtle energy wavelengths as possible can be set up. For example, a priest and priestess can set up more power if they bear ritual weapons of complementary genders. The priestess takes the sword, and the priest the cup. This can be increased further if they reverse quarters, priest in the north, the priestess in the south.

At all times, the masculine and feminine qualities of the adept should qualify and support each other, taking precedence as necessary. The magickian must have the ability to be passive for clairvoyant work, or active when casting circle, shifting states easily and completely. Qabalistically, this is the process of becoming the Tree of Life. The aim of the occultist should be to use the force of the dark and light pillars equally within the self, selecting sephirothic powers as required but never making the mistake of being limited to any one zone. Alan Richardson in his book, *Gate of Moon*, explains this, 'The Spheres describe function not status . . . A Priest of Mars is as potent as a Priest of the Moon but in a differing way.'

On a practical level, understanding the bisexual self may

mean overcoming emotional and psychological conditioning. Stereotyped reponses to male and female take many forms, particularly when a person's background has familiarised them with certain patterns of behaviour, the so-called 'norm', 'women wash dishes', 'men don't cry'.

In a close-knit magickal group problems of this sort will emerge quickly. For instance, a man who has previously considered himself well adjusted may suffer from homophobia when the psyche expresses attraction for a person of the same physical gender as its host. In the company of gay people, the homophobic male displays righteous indignation, a reaction which H.G. Wells describes as 'jealousy with a halo'. This reaction is a conditioned response, designed to prevent the individual feeling any emotion, such as affection, towards another male. It is important to love and respect a person as a person and not restrict affection to another because of their gender. In saying this it is important to remember that terms such as affection do not necessarily imply a sexual relationship. In a group, the law of polarity must also apply to physical gender but any restrictive moral codes, such as compartmentalising people only by gender, will serve to damage the group.

Similarly a man can exhibit conditioned responses in relationships with women, particularly to a priestess, which superficially appear correct and supportive. The facts, however, may be different, and the actions may be an overcompensation for his fear of the active woman. His adopted persona is that of the 'knight in shining armour'. These attitudes continue the double standards of Victorian morality by ignoring the true nature of woman.

Women also suffer from conditioning although they appear to suffer less from intrinsic sexual problems. Even in today's society, many women still find it difficult to break out from the mould of passive wife and mother, although often showing great reserves of strength which could be used. In the situation where the man in a relationship is worried about his wife's participation in occultism, through

69

his own insecurities, women often feel forced to choose between magick and the assumed security of a relationship. By lacking a sense of self worth, many women do not have the necessary motivation to become seriously involved in magick for any length of time. Those who do take up this commitment often fall into the trap of developing ego-centred power fantasies, as the discovery of their positive self swamps the unprepared woman, who was previously limited to playing a passive submissive part. The guilt created by this apparent change of role can in some women cause serious psychological difficulties. Over recent years we have met a number of unfortunate people who have fallen prey to just such difficulties to the extent that they sincerely believe themselves the human avatars of well known and usually 'popular' occult forces, such as Morgana, Babalon, Therion, Merlin, and others.

Many good magickal groups have emerged as mainly goddess orientated, often with ecological and political aims. Few of these organisations are exclusively female but their aim is to reinstate the feminine characteristics in society and often to perform a useful social and supportive role.

Their aims vary from ritual magick to the celebration of women's mysteries, as in pre-Christian cultures. These groups, common in the United States and Germany, are often heavily influenced by the writings of Starhawk and other similar writers. Whilst some useful literature has grown from the Women's Movement itself, as a magickal system, a women's group must express polarity at an internal rather than physical level. Women have a fundamental advantage in the occult because they seem naturally more aware of the male and female polarity within them.

In the same way the word goddess contains the word god within it (as the divine child or 'Son of the sun'), so many women can focus on this intrinsic polarity. This is not to say that women are 'above' ritual or would not find it a useful experience.

Sadly, relatively few women become deeply involved in magick but it is clear that once the current of Wicca and magick regains its balance, more women will become involved in the occult.

One of the most important aspects of magickal sexuality is the question of occult partnerships. The term occult partnership covers various relationships, from that between a new group member and the group leaders, to that of High Priest and High Priestess in Tantric magick. The relationship between a new initiate and group leader should be a positive sharing of knowledge. If the relationship fails, the High Priestess can become a classical Freudian mother figure. The relationship can become one of teacher and pupil where the priestess inadvertantly assumes the role of guru. Keys can be given but the neophyte must be the one to unlock the doors.

The question of relationship in the sense of working partners is much more complex. In a group, a man and woman may choose to work together in rituals, study and learn magick together. This partnership need not be a sexual one although affection is bound to grow between the partners. In theory a working partnership can exist quite happily between mother and son. A working partnership must, like any magickal relationship, be based upon the concept of 'Perfect Love and Perfect Trust'.

Difficulties occur in these relationships when the terms of the partnership are misunderstood by one or both partners. Tension can occur when the participants begin to work a more intense current of magick and misconceptions of the word and implication of 'love' can occur.

One cannot apply the morality of the mundane world to magick, or equate love with marriage, sexuality, or similar values. A distinction should be drawn between a working and a magickal partnership.

The relationship between a High Priest and High Priestess should be a magickal partnership. This relationship can be a good deal more intense than the former type. Acting as more or less permanent channels for the higher self, each will see the other as the embodiment of the god and goddess. It is important that both realise that their companion is also human and not a perfect divine force. Naturally, the High Priest and Priestess will be closely in tune with the tides of the sun and moon through magickal work, and each partner should be aware of the changes of mood, sexual drive, and so on, that will naturally occur during these cycles. We would like at this stage to point out that regular magickal working has the effect of causing a rise in the hormone level of the occultist. Also it is our experience that working increases physical fertility in both men and women, and even priestesses who have been advised that they are infertile have been known to conceive.

A magickal relationship need not imply that the partners are bound to be faithful, in the patriarchal sense, to each other. It may on occasions be more correct for partners who are used to each other to work with a different partner. For this reason the spark of love should be common between all members of the group, and any restrictive feelings such as jealousy or resentment will only serve to harm the group.

The relationship between the High Priest and High Priestess should be such that they form a foundation for the group. In any case the partners should trust each other to know that any other relationship necessary within will not jeopardise their partnership. The leaders of the group must stand united in 'Perfect Love and Perfect Trust'. In any case personal feelings must always come second to any magick in hand and the Great Work as a whole.

The members of any partnership (the essence of magick being change) may decide to terminate their relationship and go their separate ways. Whilst in some cases this can be difficult it would be foolish to continue a commitment to another person which restricts individual growth. In Wicca, any magickal partnership can be made for a year and a day and can be renewed once this time limit has expired without any lessening of the depth of commitment.

As the individual becomes involved with magick at a deeper level, so he or she will discover that close relationships with others not sharing a commitment to the occult path will become increasingly difficult. The psychic linking of minds is necessary, and whilst this is most important in sexual relationships, the magickian will find it true in all spheres of life. The desire for a mental link with others limits those the occultists can be truly at home with. There is often a considerable difference in ethics and lifestyle between an occultist and one who does not share the same world view. We would like to emphasise that the magickian cannot be aloof from everyday existence but the above factors should be considered. Nor must the magickian appear superior to others: being grounded in this reality is necessary to prevent ego-centred fantasies flourishing.

Ideally it is the magickal group that gives the magickian the necessary support, and a chance to work with and simply talk to like-minded individuals. The High Priestess and High Priest should be the leaders of the group basing their authority on 'Perfect love and Perfect Trust'. The magickal group is the modern form of the prehistoric tribal gestalt. Ideally, all the group members should reach a stage where formal direction of 'what to do' by the leaders becomes unnecessary, and the group's telepathic interlinking is complete. All energies owe their ultimate origin to the sexual current.

CHAPTER 6
THE PURPOSE OF THE SABBATS

'The Magician must build all that he has into his pyramid, and if that pyramid is to touch the stars, how broad must be the base!'
Aleister Crowley, Magick

The preceding chapters have been an attempt to explain the foundation of magick both in terms of human history and psychic development. We have itemised some of the problems and discrepancies of modern occultism which have led us to evolve our own system. In Chapter 9 are examples of our rituals which are the synthesis of our research into many diverse magicultures, both old and new. They are our attempt to express the structure of our system in a manifest way. The symbolism of these rites is, we have found, the most effective means of applying the structure of the Serket archetypes and wheel of the year in a human context. All magickal groups should engage in research into their chosen system of magick, as well as into a variety of cultures and traditions in order to distil a complete and viable pattern of ritual. Here the intent of the group is paramount. The system used must be conducive to the aim the group is working towards. The end product need not be the same as that given here but the results should be built on firm foundations of understanding.

In the writing of a ritual, the most important consideration is intent — having explored the karmic consequences of the rite, the most effective method of reaching your chosen objective must be found.

By the use of the word system with reference to Serket, we do not mean to imply that it is a sacred litany that will never change. Even without major alterations to a system it is often necessary to change a principle rite, such as a Sabbat. This may need to be done for many reasons, practical or magickal. It is also important to remember that in any group there are individuals who react differently to different currents.

A lunar clairvoyant will require more personal preparation, for example meditation, if the participants in the ritual are all solar fiery people, who are less naturally attuned to this type of working. More 'violent' occult forces, such as Pan or Sekhmet, must be handled with extreme care, and only invoked on a magickian who will not snap under the onslaught of such a powerful energy. If a magickal group is working a balanced current of energy then they will naturally tend to 'call in' people with dramatically different but complementary talents. Such a group will tend to be made up of equal numbers of both male and female magickians both 'positive' and 'negative' priests and priestesses.

We have omitted any specifically magickal ritual from the following pages, but have included examples of our Sabbat Rites. The Sabbats are the 'high points' in our system of the year wheel, drawing together many of the fruits of our research. Each Sabbat takes a primitive, usually precultural archetype and directs its manifestation through an intellectually constructed rite.

The Sabbats operate on many levels. Firstly, their aim is to keep the participants in touch with the tides of the year, linking the macro and microcosm through the flux of the lunar and solar cycles. The second purpose of the Sabbats is to act as reservoirs of power, psychic energy sources which provide currents of force that the participants can draw upon. This helps maintain the existence of the astral group mind.

The third, and arguably most important part, is that of

initiation. Each working stimulates a different part of the self. In this way each individual will experience a different initiation depending on how high is their level of awareness, and this will occur in a way which will benefit the person most in self evolutionary terms.

This is not to say that anyone can be allowed into such a circle, as the psychological shock of facing a previously hidden facet of the self can be difficult for those without the necessary level of awareness and courage.

The fourth purpose of a Sabbat is expressed in the sharing of wine and food following the rite itself. This was a forerunner of the Christian mass, and not a parody of it. As well as stimulating a group bond this part of the Sabbat allows the energy raised in the circle to go to work. The seed planted by the rite begins to gestate and the grounding of the participants by the use of food and drink helps to earth the power and bring it to manifestation. The energy of a Sabbat can be directed to any goal but because of its potency it will react in all levels of the magickian's life, material, mental, and astral.

The rituals reproduced in Chapter 9 are only the skeletons of the Sabbats. They are the words that are said and the actions performed but cannot convey the energy behind the rite.

The High Priest and High Priestess must, with the help of the group, turn a set of ideas on paper into an effective current of magickal reality. They may find it necessary to make changes during the work itself, gauging the reactions of the participants. The group leaders must work with their experience, logic, and intuition, timing the raising of energy and delivery of invocations for maximum effect. The act of ritual lifts the veils between levels of reality until what at first may seem a simple dramatic act, for example the symbolic sacrifice of the dying god, becomes an actual event not merely a token going through the motions. Ritual is not play acting or even psychodrama, it is a potent energy which must be used wisely.

The ritual used by some primitive tribes consisted of various methods generally labelled Shamanistic. Those techniques included the use of alcoholic drink, chanting and drugs, such as peyote or amanita. Drama was another ritualistic key involving the use of imposing ritual masks and indeed sleight of hand, on the part of the Shaman, in order to instil the feeling of awe necessary to raise energy.

Our methods draw from these practices, including them and omitting them as we feel necessary to achieve the aim of a given rite. Certain shamanistic techniques are no longer viable due to both cultural and legal changes in society, such as the use of some drugs.

Within our ritual structure we have used the law of magickal correspondences whilst not adhering rigidly to any set system of colours, planets, deities, and so on. We have found that basic planetary correspondences have proved most effective. The use of correctly formulated incense, appropriately coloured candles and temple decoration are vital to stimulate the subconscious. Jewellery and particularly headress (robes if worn) can add substantially to the feel of the ritual and increase the individual's involvement.

The following is a summary of other methods we have used within our system some of which are perhaps less well known.

Preparation for a circle on a psycho-physical level is as important as the practical preparation of your working site. In many forms of Christian and Eastern occultism, fasting is used as an extreme form of ascetism and self-denial prior to esoteric work. In our opinion, fasting as a long-term practice only serves to weaken and possibly damage the physical body with little spiritual benefit.

There are circumstances when fasting together with abstinence from sex and non-medicinal drugs, such as tobacco and alcohol, in varying degrees may be a useful exercise in pre-initiatory work and testing the will. Purification of this type may last up to one lunar cycle. Preceding a ritual we often suggest a limited form of this for twenty-four hours prior to the working, as this heightens the senses and makes the food and drink consumed in the circle more potent (refer to the Beltaine Ritual on page 111).

Some practices should always be adhered to, such as the writing of a magickal diary by each individual.

Before commencing, the wording of the rite is read through in the presence of the group members. At this point participants can make final comments, or make requests for specific work to be done. This is also the point of no return and is the final opportunity for those who, for whatever reason, do not feel they can participate to express this. Beginners are given detailed information on the circle so that they have a complete idea, at least physically, of what to expect. With more advanced group members, who have more trust in the High Priest/Priestess born of experience, the element of surprise can be put to dramatic effect. In a pathworking, for instance, the magickians should not be given too much information on the nature of the exercise by the leaders. In this way the participants' minds are not cluttered with knowledge of what they 'should' see. It is also a test of trust between the leaders and the group and vice versa.

Surprise, perhaps tinged with positively expressed fear, acts like any power-raising technique, quickening the blood and stimulating the flow of adrenalin.

Another method based on the surprise technique is selective admission to the circle. Keeping group members outside the temple has two purposes. Firstly, it helps to make entry to the room more dramatic.

The location is no longer simply part of a house it is a focal point of power to be entered with reverence and commitment. Secondly, it allows the temple to be set up by those already within the circle. This can include the use of lighting, flowers, ritual makeup on the participants, and so on. In this way the group leaves a simple room to return finding it transformed into a place of magickal reality. This method can also be used in reverse, the priestesses being admitted to the circle once they have completed their preparations, such as symbolic make-up, jewellery and robes.

On certain occasions we have found changes in lighting useful. The best illumination to work by is half-light. Texts can be read by the light of an altar candle held by an assistant, or memorised if need be. The lighting in the temple can also be changed by the extinguishing or lighting of candles; changes of incense during different phases of the rite can also be employed.

The use of make-up in ritual is an ancient technique. Make-up can dramatise, or be used to focus the mind on one specific cultural form (Egyptian, American Indian, Pre-Celtic) if necessary, for example khol eyeliner, blue body markings. Make-up can also be used to suggest atavistic forms, the cat, the serpent (for which 'body glitter' is ideal), the hawk, etc. It can also be used symbolically, as in marking the body with an appropriate sigil such as a serpent or crescent, often on the forehead. A symbol on the body, particularly that of the High Priestess, can be used as a focus in Tantric magick; often the sigil of the rite's aim is drawn between her breasts. Anointing with make-up designed to simulate blood or the pallor of death is also effective.

Music and dance traditionally played an important part in magick. Chanting, mantras and even 'sonic languages', such as Enochian, help stimulate the subconscious and lull the mundane mind. Drum music is most effective in raising power, from slow rhythmic beating to fast ecstatic dance. Dance after a rite is also beneficial, serving to release and channel energy raised by the rite, particularly if taken to the point of exaustion, and to help shake off any heavier energy that may be raised in powerful magickal work. It can be used symbolically during a ritual, as in the maze dances, wheel dance, or hunting dance of the King Stag. The dance should flow with the music, the steps being improvised by the participants. Dance can also be used to generate a trance level if taken to an extreme.

Physical effort is another useful means of raising energy. Mental exercises are doubly powerful when linked with a physical act. This is the same principle used in Tantric sex magick. In 'cord' magick the participants must pull hard on the cords so they are held taut across the circle.

In the psyche, the pull on the cords is proportional to the energy raised. This is an early method of sympathetic magick similar to that used in early fertility cults. The process of using the physical and magickal bodies in unison is the founding principle of Western occultism. The most potent magickal methods are those which stimulate different levels of the adept's being into simultaneous action.

The Sabbats have best effect if the group meets on other dates as well. Magick like any art is strengthened by regular practice. Other meetings should coincide with suitable phases of the moon. These other meetings can take the form of training circles, pathworking exercises, or be used as occasions for magickal work.

Each of the four major Sabbats relates to a phase of the moon (refer to the wheel of the year, Figure 3 on page 81). By working magickally through a period of a month, the experience of the lunar phases can be encapsulated within the Sabbat rite. Thus the lunar month forms the microcosm of the year's cycle. In our system, wherever practical, the four major Sabbats are celebrated during the correct lunar phase.

In Serket, a sexual formula is ascribed to each Sabbat (see pp. 102–29). It is important to stress that it is not the physical Tantric rite that is important but rather the quality of the energy raised. For instance, Imbolc is ascribed the mystery of the 'serpents tongue', that is to say oral sex performed on the Priest, or more often the Priestess, in order to induce oracular states. This is the Sabbat of the Delphic Pythoness, the Priestess who 'sees' clairvoyantly with her 'eye', the pineal or ajna chakra (Kenneth Grant's works provide more, if somewhat occult information on this method). This does not mean to say that the sexual act, if

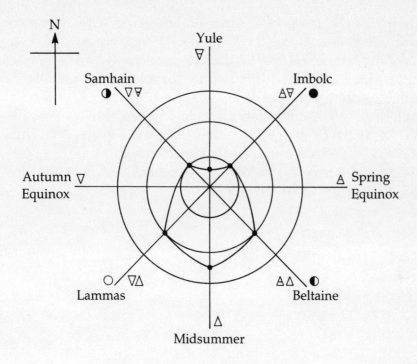

Figure 3. The wheel of the year as the magick circle. Each of the eight main directions is ascribed a Sabbat, also an elemental classification and a lunar phase

any, performed using this current, need involve physical oral sex. It is the psychic force raised that is important, not the method of intercourse.

It should also be clear to any magickian that the term 'symbolic' used within a ritual framework does not rob any practice of its validity. No occultist who has contacted, say, the Sekhmet force through his or her symbolic keys, would fail to testify to the crystal clear reality of that power. Remember that ceremony, of any type, is a means to an end, not an end in itself. Gerald Gardner in a coded passage from his book of shadows calls ritual a '. . . system of props and aids . . .' At the same time ritual can be potent, and the daring of the magickian must be tempered with necessary prudence.

Above all, ritual, particularly a Sabbat, should be enjoyable. Magick can be difficult to perform but it should also be fun. Genuine laughter is always the best form of magickal defence. The occultist should remember the words of the Wiccan Charge which advises 'Mirth and Reverence'. Thus a good magickal group is one whose rites grow from knowledge and a joyous spontaneity, coupled with a respect for the potent forces involved.

CHAPTER 7
THE FOUR-FOLD GODDESS

'At the core of the Bright Mother is the Dark mother, and at the core of the Dark Mother is the Bright Mother.'
Janet *and* Stewart Farrar, Eight Sabbats for Witches

The goddess has four major aspects. She can be symbolised in many ways but in each case the message is the same. If we express the goddess in terms of the seasons, it becomes apparent that her four-fold nature has, in modern Wicca, been reduced to three; this omission is apparent not only in simple symbolism but also in the way certain areas of her mysteries have been deliberately ignored (see Chapter 4). The Maiden goddess is spring, the Mother is summer, the Hag is autumn, however there does not appear to be a suitable attribution for winter. This gap in the chain of correspondences is most dramatically expressed when the goddess's aspects are viewed alongside major elements in Craft and magickal symbolism, for example four major Sabbats, four quarters, four magickal initiations, etc. There are four magickal abilities of the adept: to Know, to Will, to Dare, and to Keep Silent. The four-fold goddess also corresponds to the four esoteric or alchemical processes: Creation, Sustenation, Destruction, and Putrefaction. These correspondences are illustrated on pages 175 and 177.

The moon has four faces. Three are visible but when the moon is dark (secret) it is still present. The three-fold goddess is based on the neglect of the 'dark moon'. Confusion has also arisen with the identification of the goddess with other deities, such as the three Fates, the three Norns, etc. R.J. Stewart's book, *The UnderWorld Initiation*, explains how this arises: 'Revivalist pagan cults often fall into the metaphysical trap of believing that all Female Innerworld Beings are the Goddess . . .' Other evidence can be found in the construction of goddesses such as Hecate, originally the Egyptian Heqet, who was goddess of the crossroads.

Her image is often that of three women; the fourth is invisible (as the dark moon) because she hides behind Hecate's Mother, or full moon aspect. It is also true that the Mother aspect of the goddess was both 'beautiful and terrible', that is to say containing both the sustaining light force and its complementary dark force of putrefacation and reabsorbtion.

The goddess with four faces directly interrelates with the concept of the major subelements (air of earth, air of fire, water of fire, and water of earth) and many other systems. In another sense, the goddess can be seen in the solar cycle. She is sunrise, noon, sunset and the hidden 'sun at midnight', symbolised in Egypt by the dark goddess, Bast.

The goddess is also constant: in her guise as the four seasons she is the earth showing different aspects but remaining stable. By the same token the god has two forms, one 'solar' and one 'lunar'. Using the above analogy the god rises and falls as do the luminaries, the sun and moon, but the goddess is continuous, simply adopting different masks. To paraphrase a remark made by one of our group, 'The goddess is like a tree and the god like the leaves. He grows, comes to fruition, dies and is reborn but the tree itself is eternal.' The goddess is passive or receptive in her dark and waxing aspects. Here she symbolises potential energy. She becomes active in her full and waning form, where she is kinetic energy. In Egyptian mythology, the goddess Bast is her potential form and Sekhmet her kinetic aspect. This is shown by the way Bast has rulership over the internal process of pregnancy, while Sekhmet presided over the bloody sexual act of childbirth.

84

The godforce is defined as a partnership, a dual lunar and solar deity. These forms are directly related to the brothers Set and Horus in Egyptian mythology. In later cultures, the positive interaction of these energies is misinterpreted as a battle between the forces of dark and light.

This is another unfortunate result of Zoroastrian belief incorrectly applied to magick. The lunar god, symbolised by the serpent, is the dark hidden energy, the waning or dark phase, he is Hoor-paar-Kraat. His energy is constant but only emerges at certain times in the year's cycle.

The solar form of the god, symbolised by the eagle, plays a different role. He is born of the goddess, and rises absorbing the power of his dark self. He becomes King of the Earth, fertilises the goddess and is then reabsorbed. During this process the eagle hands back authority to the lunar god. This solar deity is Ra-Hoor-Khuit, the waxing and full phases of power. In many ways the eagle is the child of the goddess and his lunar counterpart. The solar god fertilises the earth, whereas the serpent fertilises the goddess herself so that she may bring forth her bright consort. The eagle rises and descends but the serpent is either absorbed into the form of the eagle or stands apart from him (in the period between Samhain and Imbolc).

There is a natural period during which this change takes place. This occurs at the time of the equinoxes, which our system uses for magickal work, rather than Sabbat celebrations. The equinoxes are points of change not within the cycle of the year but within the solar and stellar spheres. The serpent is also the archetype of the magickian, as mediator between levels of reality. This deity is more a she–male or hermaphrodite rather than simply an aspect of the god force.

This cycle can be completely expressed as in Figure 4 on page 86, which represents the Serket Wheel of the Year. These cycles, once locked into by the Magickian's self, will also act on a personal level. In the same way that each occultist has a personal archetypal or atavistic form, so in a

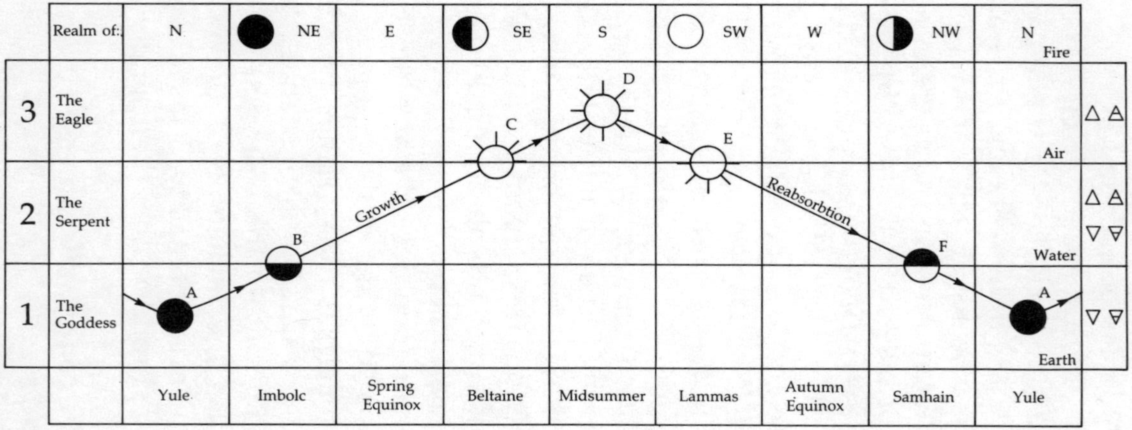

Realm of:	N	NE	E	SE	S	SW	W	NW	N Fire
3 The Eagle								●	Air
2 The Serpent		◑ B	Growth	◐ C	◯ D	◯ E	Reabsorbtion	● F	Water
1 The Goddess	● A								● A Earth
	Yule	Imbolc	Spring Equinox	Beltaine	Midsummer	Lammas	Autumn Equinox	Samhain	Yule

Figure 4. The four-fold goddess — the same yearly cycle as depicted in Figure 3 but in a horizontal format

group it is often found that the priests begin to identify directly with either the solar or lunar god. Also the priestesses will often be most attuned to one of the four aspects of the goddess. The High Priestess following the nature of her role will usually adopt one of the goddesses' more active forms.

A specific role adopted by an individual in a rite will also have personal consequences as the magickal level interacts with the individual's mundane life (for example, the part of the stag in the Beltaine rites, see page 110). In a powerful group it is necessary that all the members should be able to function as High Priest or High Priestess as necessary. In many ways the physical act of leading a rite is one of the least important parts of group leadership and one that can, in a good group, be surrendered as required without any loss of authority. The group members will have natural specialisations but each member should be aware that even in a group it is this very 'shifting of spheres' that gives the circle a dynamic stability.

The rites in Chapter 9 are based on this structure. Introductions are given explaining the 'side' of symbolism chosen for each Sabbat. Part of the practical structure of these rites is based on the limitations and advantages of our own group, such as the number, experience and particular talents of the individuals concerned. We do not feel it necessary to give detailed information on procedures such as casting the circle. This information is available in many forms in many books and although we have simplified and rewritten part of this rite, the basic framework remains intact.

Figure 4 on page 86 shows the same yearly cycle as depicted in Figure 3 but in a horizonal format. The undulating line represents the flow of power through the year, which, as it progresses, takes on different aspects. It also represents the path of the fertilising Eagle God through the three realms described below (the numbers, 1–3, correspond to those on the left-hand side of the figure):

1. The underworld is the dominion of the goddess in her most obvious manifestation. However it is also the point in which the serpent power is at its most potent.

2. The middle ground represents the earth, the stage for the transition between different states.

3. This section represents the height of the eagle's power and as such corresponds to the sky.

It should be remembered that the goddess form pervades all these states but is most apparent in the first level. The lines separating each level correspond to one of the major elements.

(The letters, A–F, correspond with those marked on the figure.)

A. The Power of the Serpent is at its apotheosis. The eagle is born from the womb of the goddess. (For information on the aspect forms of the deities at each Sabbat see page 177.)

B. The eagle pledges himself as the son of the goddess to the Great Work of Light, and to absorbing the wisdom of the serpent into himself. This could be likened to the first oath and subsequent study prior to magickal work.

C. At Beltaine, the eagle symbolically absorbs the last power of the serpent (symbolised by a stag, see Beltaine rite, page 110) into himself, and begins his work of fertilisation.

D. Height of the eagle's power.

E. The eagle makes his last act the fertilisation of the goddess, with the seed that will result in his own rebirth at Yule. He hands back power to the serpent who is pledged to the goddess to perform the Great Work of Darkness.

F. The serpent completes his preparation and descends into the underworld to act as consort to the goddess and guard the seed of the eagle.

In order to pass into the underworld the serpent must surrender the eagle's magick (the knowledge of time) to the goddess who will entrap him.

This synthesised myth can be read at a seasonal, magickal/archetypal, or personal level.

CHAPTER 8
THE CIRCLES OF TIME

'Invoke Them in Darkness, Outside The Circles of Time.'
From the Qabalahs of Besqul

The seasonal festivals, in relation to magick, form one aspect of occultism which has been the subject of much research. Thanks to the late Victorian zeal for investigating rustic folklore, records of many pre-industrial-age customs have been preserved. The Sabbat celebrations have been researched and written about from many different viewpoints. It is also the case that the Sabbats are a subject regularly dealt with in occult works, particularly those concerned with modern witchcraft. Therefore, in this chapter we intend to deal with the more arcane aspects behind the Sabbats and in particular the importance of the Sabbats within the esoteric view of time.

The passage of the year is, as with the goddess image, based on a four-fold cycle of birth, fertilisation, death and putrefaction. It is this cycle which our ancestors observed in nature, personalised into the mythology of the gods and expressed as the wheel of the year. Ancient civilisations were profoundly concerned with the nature and measurement of time itself. The relics of this interest are quite apparent, in heiroglyphic texts, ancient buildings, and other archaeological evidence. Whilst much consternation still surrounds the purpose of constructions such as Stonehenge and around Avebury, archaeological and esoteric evidence supports the theory that these places were used as observatories. Here early peoples were able to observe the stars, planets, the sun and moon — the cosmic bodies which first regulated the rhythms of time.

The antiquity of humanity's concern with time, as measured by heavenly cycles, is unquestionable. Alexander Marshack discovered the existence of a lunar calendar in the scratches of a bone found in Ishango, on the Nile, estimated to be 8500 years old. Most prehistoric buildings and stone circles are orientated to particular events in the celestial chronometer. The Newgrange tumulus, situated near Drogheda in the Irish Republic, was constructed in about 3250 BC, and is directly aligned to the midwinter sunrise. (Newgrange was built some 500 years before the Great Pyramids, and is thus the oldest intact building of its kind on earth.) The great temple of Karnack in ancient Egypt is aligned both to the midsummer sunset and to the rising of certain stars. The energy patterns which interact between the stars, sun, moon and earth form a whole branch of occultism. The ancient Egyptians were particularly adept at this magick, devising detailed star maps and developing a stellar calendar by which to time their magickal/religious rites.

As with the interpretation of Egyptian magickal texts by scholars with little knowledge of the occult, the scientific interpretations of these ancient calendars is often biased. Historians have claimed that these structures were used to determine the end and beginning of the agricultural seasons. Janet and Colin Bord in their excellent book, *Earth Rites*, argue that early humanity had no need of megalithic buildings to measure time for this purpose. They contend that time reckoning for agricultural purposes was achieved through a combination of 'hedge-row lore' and intuition. As Janet and Colin Bord explain, ancient people were much more aware of the tides in nature than present day industrialised societies. Some isolated communities in South America and Africa still retain an instinctive knowledge of when certain plants will come to fruition, and the movements of food animals, without the need for calendars.

There was no need for vast stone calculators to indicate the correct time for ploughing, reaping and so on. It is here that a directly esoteric approach to the information can provide the solution. Certainly our forebears did not need to know the appropriate time for sowing from a megalithic circle. What they did need to know, or rather what the priesthood needed to know, was the exact moment of each shift in the earth's energy patterns. A fundamental law in occult thinking is that everything in the universe is inter-connected: the earth and the sun, the moon and the crops, the stars and the oceans.

Human beings are the connecting strand for this principle of 'As Above, So Below'. Astronomically aligned temples, stone circles and the rest, were used to determine periods of change. They were used to isolate instants crucial to magick-al work, known as 'in-between times'. The terms 'in-betweeness concepts' and 'neither–neither' were coined by the magickian Austin Osman Spare (1886–1956). Spare was also responsible for the rediscovery of the formula of Atavis-tic Resurgence. His life and work resulted in the highly personal and esoteric Zos Kia Cultus system. As we have explained, the Sabbat festival is not conducted in celebration of any particular period in the year, although they used to be celebrated as such. The Sabbat represents the shift of force from one magickal current to another. Thus the Sam-hain Sabbat is not a recognition of the autumn season, it is the point at which the autumn period, or, to be more specific, the harvest time, ends and the winter begins. The seasonal shift is the basis for the evolution of the Sabbats as celebrations of change, but it is the flux of macro/ microcosmic energy which coincides with these periods that is of true occult significance. It is not simply the action of the sun that causes the seasonal flux but the terrestrial and stellar currents do too. Each rhythm in the universe is inextricably interconnected; there is no separate cause and effect.

Folklore and mythology recall the importance of the 'in-betweeness concepts' that are so vital in the construction of the Sabbats, and indeed all magickal acts. References are made to the nebulous period of 'midnight', the threshold of magickal portals and the mysterious faery land in which time is meaningless. Vestigial knowledge lingers on in modern Christianity with the Christmas Midnight Mass. Symbolically, Midnight Mass represents the 'in-between' state before creation, in Christian terms the expectant eve before the birth of the Christ, who was destined to redeem mankind. This is a dim reflection of a vital esoteric theorem. The delay between the date of the winter solstice celebrations and that of modern Christmas has a firm astrological basis. The solstice is the point of greatest darkness but it is not till the 25th of December that the sun appears to be gaining in strength again, that is continuing in its apparent easterly motion along the plain of the ecliptic. The same astronomical time lag occurs between the summer solstice and 'midsummer's day'.

In order to understand the structure behind the Sabbat rites, and to appreciate the interaction of the Serketian principles of eagle, serpent and four-fold goddess, a knowledge of the 'in-betweeness concepts' is vital.

In *The Book of Thoth*, Crowley states that, 'There are only two operations possible in the universe, analysis and synthesis. To divide, and to unite. "*Solve et coagula*" said the alchemists.' In both operations the magickian and his or her power is the active element. In works of analysis, the magickal force is symbolised by the sword (as representative of Air rather than Fire), dividing, separating, and shattering the subject into its composite elements. In works of synthesis the magickal energy is represented by the cup, aborbing, combining, uniting. The interplay of magick as a current directed by the human will is that of mediator; this again links the symbolism of the serpent to that of the adept. Power flows from the great void of the macrocosm through the intention of the adept to manifestation in the microcosm.

Occult theory states that certain states in the universe may exist (or be deliberately created), which lie between levels of reality. In physical terms these periods may be determined by the motion of the stars, the moon and other bodies. Certain places on the earth's surface also have an inherent in-betweeness. In non-physical terms, in-betweeness states are those such as trances and dreaming. A primary part of magickal work is the generation of these states. The use of ritual, or indeed any technique designed to alter consciousness, is aimed at producing an area from which the adept may work. This is one of the reasons behind the construction of the circle. The magickian creates a microcosmic unit in which he or she is neither in the physical nor the non-physical worlds but able to mediate between, and affect, both. Again this theory is of fundamental importance in the rites of initiation. Witches also often speak of the energy generated by the circle as the 'Cone of Power', formed as the energy from the circle spirals up into a focus above the group.

In one sense, initiation is a constant experience for the magickian, each change of perception leading to a new point of understanding. The act of initiation is that of changing states, of passing through the 'neither' world, the period of metamorphosis, into the light of understanding.

Unlike conventional physics, the occult view of time is not of a single linear progression from the past to future. As occultism maintains that there are levels of reality which exist parallel to, but different from, the material realm, so the occult view of time considers the reality of more than the physically observable facts. The linear view of time is utilised in occultism in the calculation of planetary hours, days, and so on, but a much greater view is taken of space–time as a whole.

Philosophically, there is only an eternal, ever-present 'now', an eternal point of consciousness. Amongst occultists the most commonly used model of time is that of the spiral or helix.

Frater Achad, alias Charles Stansfield Jones (1886–1950) was Crowley's 'magickal son', and was responsible for the first research into the aeon of Maat. Describing the progression of the coming aeon(s), he alludes to the spiral nature of time: 'There is always in these mysterious cycles a certain time difference, because circles do not meet and become closed, but rather continue actively as spirals . . . We live at a mathematical point called Now in Time and Here in Space — but it can never be captured and made static; it is Ever Coming.' From the correspondence concerning Achad's research into the Maatian Aeon dated 4 April 1948, Achad goes on to say of magickians, 'And so, if we should sometimes appear to jump backwards or forwards in Time it is not surprising — though often to be wondered at.' As human evolution progresses each cycle lifts into a spiral and so events are returned to but at a different level (see Figure 5).

Achad's mention of the 'Ever Coming' refers to the constant never-ending process of evolution which is the basis of magick. Thus in the sabbatical rites there is no beginning or end, no truly 'greater' or 'lesser' sabbats, each point is an initiation on the spiral of time. In this way the magickian cannot use a standard liturgy for any one Sabbat. Each rite, although conforming to the same basic energy matrix, will require a slightly different expression at each performance. As described in Figure 5 every event in the universe occurs again and again but each time at a different level.

The image of the spiral is recalled in the maze dances often associated with the Sabbat rites. Spiral dancing often features in Wicca and folk custom, and has again be discovered in archaeology as an emblem of time. The west side-chamber of the Newgrange tumulus houses a carved triple spiral. Early labyrinthine designs, such as the rock carving at Tintagel or the meandering mounds which surround Glastonbury Tor, are also forms of the sacred spiral. This image may be a 'symbolic' model of time in occultism but that is not to say that it is merely a convenient hypo-

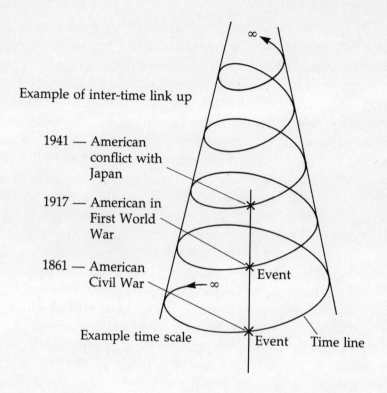

Example of inter-time link up

1941 — American
conflict with
Japan

1917 — American in
First World
War

1861 — American
Civil War

∞

Event

Event

Example time scale

Time line

Figure 5. Human evolution as a spiral pattern. Events separated by linear time are related by their vertical position on the space–space spiral

thetical form. The form of the spiral has a mathematical basis and a range of physical manifestations. In discussing the maze spirals of the Mexican Indians, geometrician and numerologist Patricia Villiers-Stuart remarks, 'To explain the workings of this number geometry in its simplest terms would be to say that it is a way of integrating the seventh and eighth division of a circle upon a square. This entails a rhythmical approach to number and shape that can be applied at one extreme to atomic structure and at the other to the stars.' The spiral manifests as the whirlpool, the DNA helix, and even in the formation of our galaxy. A spiral energy field may also be detected at certain standing stones and so we return to the monolithic construction as an image of time. The Welsh dowser Bill Lewis, and many others involved in research into ley lines, have discovered the spiral force wrapped around standing stones.

Another feature prominent in the structure of ancient Sabbat rites is that of sympathetic magick. In pagan culture the practice of dancing and love-making in the fields was common; it was reasoned that the dancing and sexual activity would liberate energy which would encourage the crops. It was the 'sympathy' between the human generative activity and the leaping dances that caused the crops to spring upward and be fruitful. Sympathetic magick is expressed as 'like calls unto like', and is thus closely related to the esoteric use of correspondences and symbolic action. That which is expressed in the microcosm will, if charged with appropriate energy, be reflected in the macrocosm.

Unfortunately little information remains, particularly in Europe, as to the precise ritual structure used by the magickians who doubtless oversaw such rites. In modern occult practice those participating in the rite are likely to be magickians only. There is no longer a situation of priesthood *and* populace providing energy, perhaps unknowingly. Our knowledge as to the construction of an appropriate Sabbat rite today must come from esoteric theory and an informed analysis of folklore and related mythology.

To recapitulate, magickal rites must be performed in areas and/or states of 'in-betweeness'. The circle of the magickian is a bubble of power which exists outside of time, and time, being an infinite spiral, can enter and influence the causal flow of the universe at any point. As with any symbolic magickal act, the generation of the spiral, such as in dance, causes a sympathy with the universal flow, which makes this influence possible.

The eight annual Sabbats are the essential rites of time. As with many occult practices, the strands can be traced throughout the English language: circle, Sabbat, serk, Circe, period, Serket, shabbat — all these words and more pertain to the cyclic, eternal, spiral, and intrinsically magickal nature of time.

KARMA AND TIME

The action/reaction principle of karmic action in occult law cannot be properly understood without an understanding of time. To take a simple linear view of karma appears to give some basis for the view that karma is force which punishes past misdeeds and rewards present goodness in the future. Rather karma is a moralistic force that occurs after the spiral pattern explained above. According to esoteric theory, at creation the individual has a predetermined True Will, albeit a True Will which must be, at some point, consciously discovered. Karma is the force that, by the action/reaction process guides the individual onto the path of his or her True Will. In Book Four, Crowley describes this process, 'A man who is doing his True Will has the inertia of the Universe to assist him. (Illustration: the first principle of success in evolution is that the individual should be true to his own nature, and at the same time adapt himself to his environment.)' Inertia in this case may be read as karma. In other words an individual who is true to his/her True Will swims with the tide of the universe rather than against it. The modern magickal attitude to karma is that it is a universal self-righting force which will only act against those who are not pursuing their True Will.

The dictum 'Every man and every woman is a star,' (*Liber AL*, *The Book of the Law*, transmitted to Crowley by the extraterrestrial entity, Aiwaz, in 1904, and reproduced in *The Holy Books of Thelema*, see Bibliography, page 180) supports the point by declaring that if, like stars, every human continues in their rightful course, then no detrimental conflicts or collisions, and therefore no karmic debts, will arise.

97

The Sabbat rites form portals into the unfolding spiral of time such that karmic situations may be resolved and analysed. Each Sabbat provides an opportunity for the adept to step outside karmic time and observe. There is a problematic correlate to this. As stated above, activity within an area charged with power, and isolated from the apparent flow of time, cannot help but influence both the adept and the universe at large. It is for this reason that the magickian must be in command of all actions within the circle, and the rite performed must be correctly constructed. Many magickal accidents are caused by ill-advised ritual statements or actions. Oaths and promises made 'in circle' should always be carefully considered.

TIME AND TIDE

Each aspect of magick is interconnected with all others. It is for this reason that the elements of cause and effect cannot be separated within a magickal operation. Linear models representing the flow of a magickal operation may be developed but essentially the timelessness of occult forces means that no event can be isolated from those that preceed, follow, and relate to it. This is particularly true with the magickal approach to the timing of rituals. For instance, a healing ritual designed to destroy a cancer would be conducted during the last days of the waning moon. Such a rite might, if a Martian force were to be used, be conducted on Tuesday and during the planetary hour of Mars. How is it that the moons' phase may assist this operation?

The forces of sympathy undoubtedly play a part, as do the effects that the moon has on the psycho-physical body of the adept. Therefore one may assume that the celestial conditions are a cause which assists the ultimate success of the work, and that these periods are not mere psychological tricks. Considerations such as days of the week and planetary hours are less vital than the luminary periods. This is

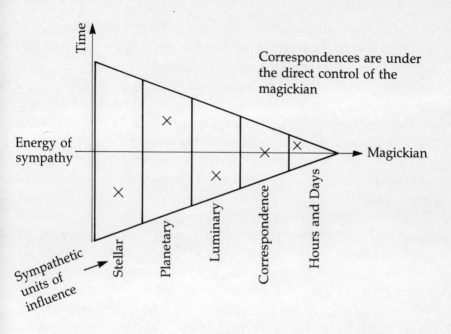

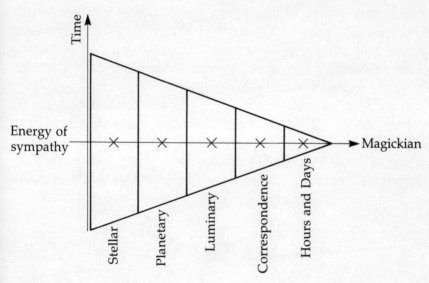

Figure 6. By awaiting the correct time, subtle forces can be aligned for maximum effect. An awareness of astrological factors is appropriate here

because the influence of the sun and moon is of direct importance to the various bodies (physical and subtle) which comprise the human organism. Smaller periods of influence, such as the planetary days and hours, are of less importance. This is also true of cosmic events (such as the movements of the outer planets and the stars) which have a less direct influence upon the adept's work.

Whilst cosmic events of a vast and comparatively small magnitude have less importance when considered individually, combinations of events may be of great significance. This is demonstrated in astrology in particular. The movements of the distant planet Pluto are generally concerned with the lives of groups or generations, and tend to be of little importance to the individual. However, the prognosis from an individual's birth chart, in which Pluto is closely related ('aspected' to use astrological terminology) to the inner planets, will be heavily influenced by the vibrations of this distant world. It is the 'line up' of forces in magick that creates most power. When the influences of the planets, moon and stars are combined with the sympathetic day, time, perfumes, colours, sounds and physical locations, then great forces may be awakened.

Four of the Sabbats are directly related to the rhythm of the moon (Samhain, Imbolc, Beltaine and Lammas), four with the powers of the sun (Yule, Spring Equinox, Midsummer, and Autumn Equinox). Each rite is 'positioned' in such a way that it is 'in-between' and automatically aligned to the immediate energy governors, the sun and the moon.

TIME TRAVEL

The magickal circle is a unit in which the adept may stand outside of time. Although referred to as a circle, the area in which the adept works is in fact a sphere of energy identical to that of the human aura. It is also possible for the occultist to select, enter and influence any point in the spiral of time.

This ability is particularly important in the Sabbat rites in which the formula of atavistic resurgence is used. During the fragile 'in-betweeness' of the Sabbat night, the adept may breach the boundaries of time and reach into the distant past or the far future. A major part of the external work of the magickian is projected forward into the future. Naturally any 'interference' in the stream of causality must be undertaken with extreme care. Event investigations into past lives (one of the practices often best attempted at Samhain) can cause repercussions by drawing the events of one life closer to that of another and causing a karmic 'short circuit' in which past events may be repeated again and again.

The understanding of time is one of the most profound occult mysteries, mysteries which the Sabbats are designed to bring into focus.

CHAPTER 9
THE SABBAT RITUALS

'When you lift the Veil of the Virgin Isis you find she is Babalon the Whore.'
Dis

The following are copies of our lunar sabbat rites. The term 'lunar' refers here to the fact that these festivals are points which refer to seasonal changes (see the correspondence information on our 'Wheel of the Year diagram, Figures 3 and 4 on page 81, and later on page 86) rather than astronomical events, such as the pattern of the sun solstices and equinoxes. In Serket, we have, where practical, calculated the time of the Sabbat's performance by the moon. For example, Lammas is the Sabbat which expresses the energy of the full moon, the best time to work this Sabbat would be the closest full moon to 31st July. If this date canot be met another should be chosen *after* the correct time. The Sabbats are peaks of power which arise to re-energise the waning power of the previous Sabbat tide. To work before the actual Lammas date would mean the rite would be tapping the lowest ebb of the Beltaine tide.

It is also important to take note of the prevailing planetary positions at the time of the rite as this can help both in preparing the rite and judging in what way the current of force will manifest. The solar Sabbats should obviously be held if possible at the correct astronomical dates.

The process of encapsulation within Serket means that by working (or simply living) magickally through the period of a month, the experience of the whole lunar cycle can be drawn upon in the Sabbat.

Thus Lammas can bring out the full moon experience but at the same time this expression is completed by the individual's understanding of the other phases of the moon (and therefore the self). In this way all aspects of the goddess power are present in the rite simply shifting emphasis from one part to another.

CASTING THE CIRCLE

This rite has been dealt with in numerous books. We employ a simplified version of the Wiccan circle casting, the basic format of which is as follows.

All the participants 'centre' at the altar. This means that each person moves out of the circle (remembering to move clockwise or 'deosil' in the same direction as the sun's movement) and kneels before the altar. The hands are placed either side of the pentacle, and a few moments are spent in meditation to focus the mind on the work about to be undertaken and the rising level of energy within the individual. Once all the group has centred (the High Priest and High Priestess last) then the High Priest kneels facing east before the altar, holding the sword up towards the High Priestess who faces him. She then draws the sword out of his hands. This represents the male force giving up power to the female force. The masculine process of writing the ritual and preparing the temple is over, and the feminine magickal part of the psyche must now take control. The feminine is the gateway to magickal power, and as the female is the occult representative of this force she takes the active role in most parts of the rite.

The group then stands and the High Priestess salutes the altar with the sword. She then turns to the east and begins to cast the circle. The Alexandrian circle casting words are:

'I conjure thee, oh circle of power, that thou beest a meeting place of love and joy and truth, between the realms of gods and men, a rampart and protection that shall preserve and contain the power that we shall raise within thee.'

We tend to omit the line 'a shield against all wickedness and evil', as this implies that the circle is a fortress against malevolent forces. It is true that all manner of 'entities' can be attracted to magickal work (like moths to a candle flame) but in a correctly directed rite no force will be called that is not beneficial in terms of the ritual in hand.

As the sword moves round the circle so the participants kneel, or take the 'ritual position', sitting on both heels, back straight, hands resting on thighs. Once the circle is cast, the sword is laid before the altar, and salt and water are consecrated. The salt is formed into an inverted triangle in the centre of the pentacle this being both a simplified Earth symbol ($\nleftgtr$) and an affirmation of the link between the salt and the water (symbol ∇).

The High Priest reads the consecration of the salt as the High Priestess draws an invoking Earth pentagram over it with her athame. She than banishes the water with a banishing Earth pentagram while the High Priest reads, and then the salt is poured into the water chalice. The water is taken round the circle by one of the group starting at the east. The water is sprinkled and each participant holds out their hands to receive it; the water-bearer also marks their foreheads with an appropriate sign using the water, such as a pentagram, or equal-armed cross.

Once all members have received the water (including the water-bearer) the censer is taken round, from the east, and each participant wafts the incense towards them as it is offered. The right altar candle is then taken round in the same way, each member raises their hands towards the flame and focuses their eyes on it as it is brought before them. This process helps build up the existence of the circle on all four levels of being. The circle is already made in

Earth as the paraphernalia and participants are physical. The Earth level, represented by the salt, is linked with the Water, which represents the astral realms. Sprinkling the circle with water helps eastablish the circle's reality on the astral; this is repeated by the censer (the element of Air) and the candle (Fire).

In the circle, the left altar candle represents the energy raised, and the right candle the manifestation of that energy. A glance at these candles during the rite will objectively tell the participants how the current of force is becoming active, depending on the way the candles burn, the colour and height of the flame. One must allow for draughts from under the door!

The temple is built like a pyramid on four levels, one of which, the earth, needs no invocation as such, through which the occult force, spirit, the fifth element, can manifest.

After this the watchtowers are invoked, beginning at the east, by the High Priest and High Priestess. Generally the High Priest draws the invoking pentagram of the appropriate element with his athame towards each quarter. The High Priestess manifests his energy by drawing an invoking Earth pentagram alongside his; the words spoken are those given in the Alexandrian Book of Shadows, 'Ye Lords of the Watchtowers of the East, ye Lords of Air . . .' This acts in a similar way to the consecration of the circle by the elements by setting up portals through which the elemental force of each quarter can manifest. The ritual has numerous variations some of which are used in the following rituals. It is not adherence to the rite that is important but rather that the rite expresses what needs to be said through its performance and allows the correct magickal force to manifest.

CAKES AND WINE

The next rite follows the main ritual. It serves to consecrate the wine and close the rite's more 'formal' section.

The first consecration of wine is usually done between the High Priest and Priestess and is performed thus:

The High Priest kneels in front of the altar or the centre of the circle, and hold the chalice of wine up with both hands.

The High Priestess stands facing him and holds her athame in both hands above the chalice. As she plunges the athame into the chalice the whole group says 'As the athame is to the male, so is the cup to the female, and when conjoined become one in truth and bring about a great blessing. So Mote it Be.'

The High Priestess removes the athame, kisses the blade, lays it upon her heart and replaces it on the altar. She then kneels before the High Priest and also puts both hands round the chalice. She drinks from it and kisses the High Priest who also drinks and returns her kiss. The High Priestess again drinks from the chalice which is then passed clockwise round the circle, being passed from person to person with a kiss and the words 'Blessed Be'. The simple, but no less effective form of the Great Rite contains within it many of the 'secrets' of magick. This rite can, of course, be adapted and changed as necessary.

The wine in the chalice is usually still red wine, symbolic of blood (see Chapter 4). Wine from the first consecration should be drunk by all participants. Some wine should *always* be left in the chalice for the High Priestess, and it should never be given to her empty for three reasons. Firstly, this symbolises the completeness of the circle, which emanates from and returns to the goddess. Secondly, as a mark of respect, and thirdly because forfeits inevitably befall the person who empties the cup! One interesting property of correctly consecrated wine is that its taste is changed. It tends also not to have the intoxicating effect associated with alcohol! We consecrate all our wine and leave a small amount after the rite to be poured back onto the earth the following morning.

During our rites we have employed a number of dramatic devices but this is not to say that these methods are only psychological tricks. For instance, an incense may have a psycho-physical effect on the participants, directly linked to the ingredients in the preparation: dragon's blood stimulates the adrenal glands, whilst camphor or dittany of Crete have soporific relaxing properties. At another level these incenses form high energy structures in which the current of magickal energy invoked can be earthed. Each incense acts like a field of fertile soil, certain forces responding best to particular environments. The law of correspondences is not simply a human construct allowing us to contact the higher self. It is a universal law as immutable as the 'cause and effect' of karma.

We do not (unless any extreme 'negative' current of energy is being used) banish our circles, as we feel that the energy of a Sabbat should be such that it will not leave any harmful side effects.

These ceremonies, like the following rites, are only outline sketches and do not contain any information on the visualisation or other techniques needed to make these rites live. These abilities can only be gained with practical experience, prudent experimentation and/or tuition from an experienced, reputable group. More information about these participatory techniques will be found in Chapter 10.

IMBOLC

At Imbolc the earth is beginning to stir from sleep and spring is dawning. This Sabbat relates to the dark moon (these terms refer to aspects of the goddess, not to her lunar or solar nature and can equally be read as phases of the sun, the seasons, etc.) and is very female in energy construction.

This tide is particularly suitable for oracular work. At this time, the goddess has the serpent as her consort but she needs a priest to pledge himself to her — to become the eagle and fertilise her in the coming year. Imbolc is the night of the women's mystery, the choosing of a mate by the lady. The goddess is brought gifts by her prospective priests. The goddess asks for her gift in the form of a riddle, 'that which is most precious to her'. Gifts need not be physical — in fact it is preferable if they are not. A song, a dance, a poem may be offered, or perhaps a gift made by the hands of the priest who offers it.

In each case, the gift should represent the individual's dedication to the goddess force as an aspect of the higher self, and a medium through which to accomplish the Great Work. Forfeits are given out by the priestesses as appropriate, if the gifts are given without sufficient thought. These forfeits should be given and received in good spirit; they should be designed to instruct gently rather than 'get at' the person concerned. The answer to the goddess's riddle is the gift of life offered last by the High Priest. The initiation of this Sabbat is that of dedication, and also accepting the dominance of the feminine principle in the performance of magick.

Use first flowers if possible, e.g. snowdrops.

A Crown of Light is placed beside the altar. (This is much the same as that used in the Candlemas section of *Eight Sabbats for Witches* by Janet and Stewart Farrar.) Forfeits shall be prepared. Women present in the temple, the men let into circle by the High Priestess. The High Priest is admitted last.

The circle is cast.

Consecration of salt and water, read by the High Priest and performed by the High Priestess:

We bless this salt that its purity may aid us and its strength preserve our intent.

We command this water to be cleansed and flow without

restrictions in our service. (The consecrations given here are of our own devising. Those used by the majority of groups are often based on the consecrations from the *Key of Solomon*.)

Consecration of circle by elements — invoke watchtowers.

High Priestess invokes on herself:
'Now the tide of darkness has turned, the spring must dawn in the earth and in ourselves. We have found the wisdom of the night, and shall bring it forth by day. Now is the time that the goddess must choose a mate to aid her in the year to come. Therefore her priestesses must also choose mates. Let the spring dawn and the goddess descend that I may have her power.'
Dance: Men form an outer circle spinning deosil (clockwise), ladies form an inner circle spinning widdershins (anticlockwise). When power is raised the High Priest stops the male circle so he remains standing in the south. The male circle then opens at the north and the women go to stand before the altar.

Maiden crowns the High Priestess with the Crown of Light which remains unlit.

High Priestess reads the Charge. (The Wiccan Charge can be found in a variety of forms in almost all Craft literature. Our form is basically that reproduced in *Eight Sabbats for Witches*.)
The High Priestess says: 'Who would be chosen to be the consort of the goddess, to guard the land with her and be her mate? Who would offer that which is most precious to her?'

Gifts are offered to the goddess by each man in turn, the High Priest is last to come forth.
The High Priest kneels in front of the altar: 'I offer my blood that the land may be reborn.'

The High Priestess holds her sword over the neck of the High Priest and says, 'This priest offers to be reborn with the land.' The High Priestess removes the sword and kneels facing the High Priest.

The High Priestess invokes on the High Priest:

'He has offered his death but we take instead his life, that which is most precious to the goddess. Therefore I choose him as my mate that the powers of the god may be his.'

The High Priest lights the High Priestess's Crown of Light. They then consecrate the wine.

Coveners take up random positions in the circle.

The High Priestess says, 'Then let us spread our magick.'

The High Priest and High Priestess then dance; as each covener is touched by their 'magick' (in the form of stage glitter) they begin to dance. The Crown of Light is then symbolically burnt either in the cauldron or if possible in a bonfire or hearth.

Cakes and wine.

BELTAINE

At the Sabbat of Beltaine, the eagle god, who made his pledge to the goddess at Imbolc, is prepared to become her consort. In this rite he becomes the king whose life is inextricably linked to the land. In order to do this he must obtain power from his dark self (who takes on the form of the king stag). This ritual has its roots in the Celtic rite of kingmaking. Once the priest has brought down the king stag, he symbolically takes authority from him, in the form of his horns, the emblems of power. The priest then mates with the priestess, the representative of the land. Here the goddess takes on the form of the waxing moon, passive like the earth but still silently in control. The initiation is that of power, pure and simple.

110

The godform here is Pan (Cernunnos in British mythology) the creator/destroyer. This energy is particularly unstable; once invoked it has the potential for destruction or highly positive creation depending on the awareness of the group, particularly the High Priestess. Beltaine is the most openly aggressive current of force within the year wheel.

The 'Hymn to Pan' used here was written by Aleister Crowley.

Preparation: The High Priest and High Priestess are to decorate the temple with foliage and set up the altar while the rest of the group wait outside the temple. Quarter candles are to be set in appropriately coloured glass holders to keep the light in the temple low. All women should wear flower crowns and ribbons. Bowls of red and white ochre are to be set upon the altar along with a crown of stag horns and a veil. Serpents covered with strips of cloth should be set upon the High Priest's wrists.

The High Priest stands on the right of the altar facing north on the edge of the circle and the High Priestess in the same way on the left of the altar.

All centre at the altar.

The leading priest and priestess cast circle. (The High Priest and High Priestess remain in their positions.)

Consecration of salt and water, read by the leading Priest and performed by the leading Priestess (as at Imbolc).

They then take round the elements.

Invoke watchtowers.

The Priest kneels before the altar and the Priestess ties the stag horn crown on him. The Priest then moves to the centre of the circle and the coven encircle him. The High Priest and High Priestess turn and deliver the 'Hymn to Pan', coven repeat the 'Io Pan' parts of the invocation:

111

High Priestess:
  'Thrill with the lissome lust of the light,
    O man! My man!
    Come careering out of the night
    Of Pan! Io Pan!
    Io Pan! Io Pan! Come over the sea
    From Sicily and from Arcady!
    Roaming as Bacchus, with fauns and pards
    And nymphs and satyrs for thy guards,
    On a milk-white ass, come over the sea
    To me, to me
    Come with Apollo in bridal dress
    (Shepherdess and pythoness)
    Come with Artemis, silken shod,
    And wash thy white thigh, beautiful god,
    In the moon of the woods, on the marble mount,
    The dimpled dawn of the amber fount!
    Dip the purple of passionate prayer
    In the crimson shrine, the scarlet snare,
    The soul that startles in eyes of blue
    To watch thy wantoness weeping through
    The tangled grove, the gnarléd bole
    Of the living tree that is spirit and soul
    And body and brain-come over the sea,
    (Io Pan! Io Pan!)
    Devil or god, to me, to me,
    My man! my man!
    Come with trumpets sounding shrill
    Over the hill!
    Come with drums low muttering
    From the spring!
    Come with flute and come with pipe!
    Am I not ripe!
    I, who wait and writhe and wrestle
    With air which hath no boughs to nestle
    My body, weary of empty clasp,
    Strong as a lion and sharp as an asp—

Come, O come!
I am numb
With the lonely lust of devildom.
Thrust with the sword through the galling fetter,
All-devourer, all-begetter
Give me the sign of the Open Eye,
And the token erect of thorny thigh,
And the word of madness and mystery,
O Pan! Io Pan!
Io Pan! Io Pan Pan! Pan Pan! Pan.'

High Priest:
  'I am a man.'

High Priestess:
  'Do as thou wilt as a great god can
      O Pan! Io Pan!
  Io Pan! Io Pan Pan! I am awake
    In the grip of the snake.
    The eagle slashes with beak and claw;
    The gods withdraw:
    The great beasts come, Io Pan! I am borne
    To death on the horn
    Of the Unicorn.'

High Priest:
  'I am Pan! Io Pan Pan! Pan!
    I am thy mate, I am thy man.'

High Priestess:
  'Goat of thy flock, I am gold, I am god,
    Flesh to thy bone flower to thy rod.'

High Priest:
  'With hoofs of steel I race on the rocks
  Through solstice stubborn to equinox.
  And I rave; and I rape and I rip and I rend
  Everlasting, world without end,

Mannikin, maiden, maenad, man,
In the might of Pan.
Io Pan! Io Pan Pan Pan! Io Pan!'

The High Priestess removes her robe and picks up a drum and begins to play. The High Priest picks up his athame. The coven move from around the Priest and the hunting dance is done, the men protecting the Priest while the women draw the men away.

When the High Priest confronts the Priest he points his athame to the Priest's chest; he kneels and makes the sign of Osiris risen. The Priestess goes to the altar to remove the vessel of white ochre. The Priestess then removes the stag horns from the Priest and ties them on to the High Priest. She then whitens the face of the Priest. Both return to the circle.

The High Priestess then removes the red ochre from the altar and walks to the centre of the circle. The High Priest is anointed with it on his face, arms and breast.

The Priestess then removes the High Priest's athame and the ochre, and replaces them on the altar. She brings the drum and blows out the altar candles.

The coven face outward and they start the AUM mantra. One covener plays a slow drum beat. The Great Rite is performed.

The High Priest and High Priestess then relight the altar candles from the south candle. The coven turn to face them, and the cloth covering the High Priest's serpents is unbound. The wine is then consecrated.

Cakes and wine.

LAMMAS

At Lammas, the eagle god hands back power to his serpent self. The goddess is in her aspect of the full moon. She is the mother overseer of this 'handing back' of power. The eagle's last act is to consecrate a chalice of wine. Thus he completes his phase of the Great Work. This also symbolises the way he has fertilised the goddess so that in time she will give birth to him once again so he may rise anew. The serpent is the 'power behind the throne'; he empowers the eagle so that he then may take over and perform his role.

The serpent then pledges himself to be the female consort, as did the eagle at Imbolc. The initiation of this ritual is dedication to the darkness, as Imbolc was the dedication to the light. This is the night of the men's mystery, balancing the female power of Imbolc. The consecrations given here are of our own devising. Those used by most groups are based on the consecrations from the *Key of Solomon*.

Preparation: The temple should be decorated with suitable flowers. The cauldron should stand in the south-west, covered with a veil. Within the cauldron should be appropriate food. A priest should stand as the eagle god, and the High Priest should act as the serpent.

The women are present in the temple first, and centre themselves at the altar. The men are lead into the circle one at a time by the High Priestess, first the eagle and finally the serpent. All the men then centre themselves.

The eagle and High Priestess cast circle, the serpent supports by standing before the altar in the Blessing position: standing feet apart, arms at right angles to the body, forearms upright, hands open, palms upwards. This position directs energy outwards.

The eagle and High Priestess consecrate the salt and water, again supported by the serpent.

Selected members of the group then take round the elements.

The eagle and High Priestess invoke the watchtowers supported by the serpent. The eagle draws the invoking elemental pentagram with the wand; the High Priestess draws the invoking pentagram of earth; the serpent draws the invoking elemental pentagram with his athame.

The High Priestess stands before the altar, the cauldron is moved into the centre of the Circle. She says:
'Now the Tide of growth is coming to a close and the experience of this time begins to bear us fruit in the land and in our selves; now the pledge must be made to darkness as it was to light at Imbolc.'

She turns to the eagle, who stands beside the serpent on the south side of the cauldron facing the High Priestess, and invokes:
'King of the setting sun, father of the fruits of the earth, lord of fallen summer. I invoke thee that your power shall complete this cycle and lay the seed for that yet to arise. I invoke thee to descend upon this thy priest.'

The High Priestess is then invoked upon by the eagle and the serpent.
Eagle: 'Mother of the fruits of the Earth'
Serpent: 'Mother of the Coming Darkness'
Eagle and Serpent: 'We invoke thee to descend upon this thy Priestess.'

The coven split into two groups, the supporters of the eagle and those of the serpent. The Eagle and High Priestess move to the centre of the circle and hold the blessing position across the cauldron. The eagle supporters form a circle around them spinning deosil; the serpent circles around the inner group spinning widdershins. The serpent dances between these two rings, enticing members of the eagle's group to join his circle. When all the group are circling widdershins the serpent joins them, and when power is at its peak the serpent commands the dance to stop, he being at the north.

The eagle removes the veil from the cauldron. He and the High Priestess take the cauldron to the north. Eagle and High Priestess then consecrate a chalice of wine. The wine is passed once around the circle, drunk by the eagle and High Priestess and given jointly, with a kiss to the serpent. The eagle kneels aided by the High Priestess, head bowed as Osiris risen. This position is: standing or sitting, forearms crossed across the breast, hands open, palms against the chest. This position is used to absorb and centre energy.

The High Priestess then invokes on the serpent:

'Son of the sun, lord of the silvery moon and velvet night, who has pledged his life to rule as my dark consort, I invoke thee to descend upon this thy priest.'

The serpent and High Priestess then consecrate a chalice of wine together.

Food is then eaten from the cauldron.

Cakes and Wine.

SAMHAIN

Samhain is the time of the waning moon, hag (and therefore whore) goddess. Here the serpent god is prepared to become the consort of the dark goddess. The woman here is the active director of power with her dual gender, symbolic of her role as the passively active priestess. Unlike Beltaine, the sacrificial 'change of state' is not made in a hunt. In this ritual the god takes on the aspect of the Merlin who moves through time. The Merlin knows, and accepts, that he must

117

pass on his magick of time to the goddess (here character-ised by the figure of Nimue from the Arthurian mythos) so that she may trap him by his own magick. Here the sacrifice is completely willing, the Merlin's voluntary entombment in the crystal cave outside time (i.e. the circle) is akin to Odin's ordeal on the World Tree when he received the knowledge of the runes. Samhain is an ideal time for accessing the akashic record, particularly using the tarot, or 'Merlin's Mirror'. Samhain's power also refers to the secret scorpionic process of putrefaction. This rite divides levels of reality (of all descriptions) until the raw building blocks of energy are left to be reformed by the action of the True Will.

Samhain is the Celtic new year, and is the ideal time for resolutions for the coming year to be made. Desires for the coming year can be written on a piece of parchment and then symbolically burnt.

Preparation: Flowers of the season should fill the temple, which should be dimly lit. The horned crown (used in the Beltaine rite) should rest on the altar. Food should stand within the temple. A leading Priest and Priestess should cast circle, the High Priestess should wear a cloak or tunic, her hair should be pinned back, the High Priest should wear a cloak and bear a stave. The cauldron should be filled with water dyed black, upon which floats a little oil.

The altar shall be set in the west.

All present within the temple to centre.

The leading Priest and Priestess cast circle to music.

They then consecrate the salt and water.

The circle is consecrated by the elements taken round by the leading Priest and Priestess.

The watchtowers are invoked.

The High Priest should stand in the north, the High Priestess in the south.

The High Priest says:

'I am the Merlin, the silent wise one,
   I am the first bard of Elfane,
   I was with the first man who kindled fire,
   I was present when the first circle was cast,
   I saw the destruction of the lost continent of gods,
   I witnessed the birth and life of the once and future
King,
   I have borne a banner before Alexander,
   I have partaken of the wine in the land of Khem,
   I have fought in lands of silken sands,
   I know the names of the stars from north to south,
   I was there when Rome was raised to the ground,
   I have been at the place of the crucifixion,
   I have obtained muse from the cauldron of
Cerridwen,
   I have seen the wonders of Asia,
   I have witnessed many wars, and rulers and times of
peace,
   I move silently as a silver salmon through the net of
time,
   I have been teacher to all intelligences,
   I am able to instruct the whole universe,
   I am and shall always be,
   I am the Merlin, keeper of the magick of time,
   I conceal the seed of the mirror of true vision,
   I am invisible as a secret serpent.'

The High Priestess delivers her invocation:
'I am the Mask of the Great Goddess,
   Like the spider I weave my silken spell
   To ensnare the God by his own will,
   For his acceptance is the key to power.
   I am mistress of all that is, all that was and all that
shall be.

I am the trickster, the lover, the Dark Queen of the
Bitter Sea.

I come as a youth, sexless but all desired.
I am Nimue, the fall of the Merlin,
The very magick the god teaches shall be the charm
by which I trap him.
And he shall follow me to his death.

A willing sacrifice, trapped in time,
Between the realms of men and gods
As those this night within the circle,
Shrouded in the mists,
Until I lift the veil that the god may pass by the Gates
of Death,
Into the world of Shadow.

I am timeless, eternal,
I am the truth behind the veil of light,
I am the soul of light.
I bear the bow of Artemis, my bow is also a harp for I
am the huntress,
But I hunt by enchantment.

I fascinate and inspire fear,
I am the guardian of the Sword,
And the Grail at Midnight,
In death, by my magick, shall the god find new life,
And come to rule with me the city of the West,
My consort and bearer of the dark mirror,
Until the tide of time flows back into the dawn.'

The coven begins to circle clockwise slowly. The High
Priest gazes at each member in turn as they pass him. He
goes to stand before the altar. One person (spontaneously)
comes forward, takes the chalice off the altar, and offers it to
him. It is then replaced. Another offers the censer which is
also replaced.

The High Priestess comes forward and offers the sword.
The High Priest kneels and accepts it. The High Priestess
removes her tunic and lets down her hair. The High Priest

120

returns the sword to her, which she holds point downwards. He then ties the horned crown about her head.

Music.

The High Priestess attempts to lead the High Priest around the circle back towards the altar. The men attempt to distract him, the women attempt to help the High Priestess.

Slowly they all slip away to form a cave with raised hands arched over, around the altar.

The cauldron is moved before the altar within the cave. The High Priest lights the cauldron, which burns briefly, and says:

'Accept the mystery of the Darkness. Those who wish to lift the veil of time come forward.'

The cave splits up and those who wish to scry come forward in turn.

Cakes and Wine.

Dancing, games and jumping the broomstick.

(As a guide to the music employed in this rite we use selected Gregorian chants and sections from the album, *Alchemy*, by the Third Ear Band.)

CHAPTER 10
THE SORCERER'S APPRENTICE

The story of the Sorcerer's Apprentice is a relevant one. In it can be seen the effects of too much arcane knowledge in the hands of one with too little wisdom. Whilst the sorcerer is away, his youthful, and somewhat lazy apprentice takes it upon himself to enlist the force of a powerful spell to his own ends. He conjures a magickal broom which he commands to fill a cauldron with water, a task the sorcerer had given to his pupil. The foolhardy lad soon realises that the animation spell is out of control and the broomstick will not stop even when water floods across the floor of the sorcerer's workroom.
Similar situations may easily arise, if in less dramatic forms, for anyone who approaches the occult without first building a firm foundation of knowledge, wisdom and understanding.

The two reasons for performing magick (or indeed engaging in any form of self-development, whether that system chooses to use the word 'magick' or not) are given by Crowley:

(a) A widening of the horizon of the mind.
(b) An improvement of the control of the mind.

Both of these statements describe processes, moreover they refer to the mind of the individual. They describe occultism as a learning process and, as such, it is natural that esoteric study should begin with a series of fundamental exercises.

The analogy is simple. If one wishes to pursue the goal of running the hundred-metre sprint in the shortest possible time, then one must first train. The initial step in training must be to develop self-discipline. The individual must learn to practise regularly and with full effort. The second consideration is the gathering of information from as many diverse sources as possible. The sprinter may wish to consult the works of numerous other runners, investigate the various dietary strategies available for building up musculature. He or she will need to tackle several areas in their own make-up, which, at first, may not seem directly related to athletic performance. An excellent example of this is the way many modern runners learn relaxation techniques and 'psyche-up' methods, to help banish performance anxiety from their minds before an important race.

The same rationale is common to magick: before ascending the giddy heights of spiritual illumination one should have developed the necessary resolve and esoteric physique.

The scientific and artistic components of magickal practice form themselves into two interactive aspects of occult training. These are:

1. Acquisition of intellectual knowledge and the ability to analyse objectively any given component of the universe.

2. A widening perception of, and development of the ability to interact fully with, any given aspect of the universe.

These twin pillars may seem highly abstract, even contradictory, whereas they are in fact complementary and concrete. The basic principles of modern occult training are that an increased awareness of both the self and one's environment are necessary to formulate a grasp of the mechanism of the universe; it is this mechanism which is termed 'magick'.

The 'As Above, So Below' theorem of magick is explicitly illustrated here, as is the esoteric meaning of the word 'spirit'. Spirit is the sum of the interaction of the four elemental forces. So, in training, the individual must learn, not to eschew the physical world but to experience and use it as a tool in self-development (Earth). Sensitivity to the energies and tides in both macro and microcosm (Water) must be learnt. The ability to analyse ideas, emotions and systems must be cultivated (Air), as must the ability to direct energy and discipline the mind (Fire). Thus through interaction with the four elemental forces the individual may grow in Wisdom, Knowledge and Understanding (see page 135). It is important, and often difficult for the student of magick to understand, that the most rudimentary physical mundane things are as much a part of magick as complex Qabalistic ritual and exotic meditation techniques.

Magick is in no way aloof from 'ordinary' existence; as such it is only natural that magickal training should begin in a common-sense, step-by-step way. The same common-sense is applicable to the more 'advanced' methods of occult working, though the rationale is often more obscure. When programming a computer for the first time it may seem strange that 'words of power' such as 'GOTO 10' may produce such dramatic effects in the system, yet when the system is fully understood and the mystery revealed, then the simple logic of the program command is appreciated.

It would seem most appropriate to start with the primary magickal tool, not the sword or pentacle, but with the physical body.

It is initially through the sensory systems in the body that most information, be it empirical or qualitative, comes to the mind. The logic of occult training is therefore, in our view, to begin by learning to use the senses to the full, in a disciplined manner. Moreover, organisation of the senses requires discipline of the body; if the senses are the players, then the body is the stage.

According to the school followed there are several ways of doing this, from the exacting set of movements used in T'ai Chi Chuan to the 'total immersion in the ecstasy of divine union' in certain aspects of Tantric yoga. Developing an awareness of the body as a temple is vital to a proper magickal perception of its role. As a temple it must be appointed in such a way as to help rather than hinder the operations conducted within it.

In practical terms, the logic is that if you wish to learn, say visualisation, it is useless to do so unless you can sit still for more than five minutes. It is fruitless to try any techniques of organising the imagination, such as clairvoyance, unless you can learn to relax your physical body. Just as the runner knows the intimate connection between the state of mind and the endurance of the body, so the magickian understands the interrelationship between the physical frame and the workings of consciousness.

The basic techniques begin with learning to relax: to relax the muscles in the body, to relax the nervous system and then to relax the mind. It is from this created space within the self that the investigations of the student can proceed. When the mind is centred or 'virgin', it may be treated as a clear canvas on which the magickian may paint as he or she wills, an area free of undisciplined thought.

During the evolution of the Serket system, both in training others and ourselves, we used a number of methods, all based on the principle that by participation in the universe one may develop one's self. Many of the techniques we used were based on simple psychodrama exercises in an occult context, some of which are detailed below. However, the central technique of development contained within each exercise was to enable the individual to find what one member of our working group referred to as 'a point'; that is a singularity of perception, a point of stillness and silence, akin to the state of Samadhi or 'one-pointed awareness' spoken of in yoga.

The following will form the basis of a training programme, and an overview of the methodology and philosophy of esoteric development as we see it.

125

Mind/Body — Control Through Relaxation

Most people without any training in self-development are restless. Their minds are a confused jumble of unresolved worries, fears, hopes and desires. This is reflected in their bodies: most are unable to relax even one muscle, and thus people living in the Western industrialised world can develop stomach ulcers, heart attacks, and insomnia. Our culture lives in fear, not necessarily of nuclear catastrophe or social collapse but the fear of boredom! Douglas Adams suggests that humans always talk because they are frightened that if they shut-up their brains will start working.

Relaxation provides the key to occult power, and this paradox produces the first and most effective barrier against those who approach magick searching for riches untold, and a means of inspiring the ever-lasting love of the girl next door. Relaxation begins with control of the physical body and this can be most directly achieved by using adapted and simplified techniques drawn from the Indian yogic systems.

Practice and Perseverance

Before discussing the methodology of mind/body control there are some important considerations of esoteric training as a whole.

Magick is a discipline. Even when it involves wild dancing and drumming as a means to attaining spiritual ecstasy, control is still required. Upon taking the first steps on the magickal path, the individual will soon learn that you don't get something for nothing. Magickal exercises, like the physical training of our hypothetical runner, need to be practised with determination, tenacity, and, this is vital, regularity. Ten minutes of practice, undertaken every day for two weeks, will produce more dramatic results than irregular practice pursued over the course of a month.

In these matters it is wise for the student to remember the words of Frater Perdurabo (Crowley) written in *The Book of Lies*,

> Practice a thousand times, and it becomes difficult,
> A thousand thousand and it becomes easy;
> A thousand thousand times a thousand thousand,
> And it is no longer thou that doeth it, but it, that doeth itself through thee.
> Not until then is that which is done, well done.

In the initial phase of magickal training the student will face the most difficult test, not any Dennis Wheatley demon, but the inertia of one's own mind. Self-discipline is the most difficult discipline to cultivate but is useful in all aspects of life and vital in occult development. Even the best tutor of the magickal arts can only suggest possible inroads into the self, through the medium of practices to be used, experiences to be had, or systems to be tried. It is up to the student to pursue the courses outlined to the fullest of his or her ability.

Place and Position

In training, many considerations will be founded on the personal circumstances of the individual. Group training provides many excellent opportunities for the individual to see their own development within the context of their relationship to other people. Contrary to popular understanding, magickal development is not divorced from other people any more than it is divorced from the material world. Yet the onus of development lies on the individual and it is with the individual that the premise of magickal training begins.

The first consideration is the arena of practice. The chosen area should be free from distractions. It is possible to enter a profound state of meditation on the London underground during the rush hour but for the beginner a quiet room, warm but not stuffy, clean but not clinical, comfortable and relaxing, is essential.

Having found an appropriate space within which to work, the first thing to practise is stilling the body. Even during sleep the body may be restless and tense. The key to relaxing the body is not by blotting out the conscious mind but by awareness of it. Try it for yourself.

Begin by lying down in your chosen location. Try to lie still and relaxed for just five minutes. To do this, without shifting your weight or fidgeting, is surprisingly difficult. Learning to lie still is one of the highest accomplishments of magickal self-discipline. The trick is not to force yourself to lie still but to persist in your practice. Lie still and observe the irritations that you will find. Be aware of how your mind and body react to lying down, doing nothing. Try to increase the duration of this exercise by five-minute increments over a period of two weeks of daily practice. In doing so, you will see just what your body feels like at rest and will begin the encounter with the forces of boredom.

The mind becomes bored when the level of sensory input diminishes. The continuous stream of sensory input to which humans subject themselves acts as 'white noise', effectively screening out the signals of the self. This is not to say that sensation, even sensory overload, is a 'bad thing'. Rather it is our half-hearted appreciation of sensation that is the problem. Few people over the age of nine can enjoy simply looking at an autumn leaf for more than a few seconds, yet what a world of experience is overlooked. We pump ourselves full of a myriad experiences but on few occasions really stop to see the night sky, or listen to the sound of the ticking bedroom clock. Perceptual sloppiness makes us ignore the obvious and therefore believe that we need more stimulation not less. The cause of this is partly due to the reticular formation in the brain. It is this which acts as a censor of incoming perceptions, damping down some and heightening others. One example of this is the way a soldier can sleep through the sound of bombs and aircraft in the distance but will instantly awaken when his senses pick up the threatening sound of footsteps.

During the lying-down exercise described above, the individual will soon encounter an important lesson. The demon of boredom is clever and will, if it feels it has been thwarted, do its level best to engender any form of stimulation in the mind of the student. One of the tricks in its armory is that referred to in Zen Buddhism as 'Makyo'. That is, as defined by Lawrence LeShan, 'Makyo are illusions that we project on realities as an aid to escaping from the directions.' The boredom complex will try inducing itching sensations, cramps and even chest pains in the student and, if the student still determines to lie there, may even try to create a 'spiritual revelation'.

The story of the Zen master Dogen illustrates this. One day a student of Dogen explained to his master that, while deep in his meditations, he had seen a brilliant white light with the Buddha behind it. 'That's nice', replied the master. 'If you concentrate on your breathing it will go away.' This first trap is one of the most dangerous. It is easy for the student to find success and immediately be captured by the romance of the vision rather than the reality of the practice. A significant difficulty with learning alone is that self-discipline can easily convert to self-congratulation. It is here we come to another important discipline for the student, that of keeping a record.

Detailed recording of results forms part of the objective component of magick. By keeping a record, honestly and diligently, the student may produce a yard stick against which to measure progress. Study of one's record will provide clues as to when certain practices may be conducted with most benefit. By contemplating one's record one may find that, for instance, exercises in visualisation are better performed during the morning, while exercises of a more active type produce better results in the evening. Recording dreams in this magickal record also serves to illuminate the changes occurring in the individual's subconscious. In short, it is as foolish to do magick without method, as it were to do anything else. The magickal record is the methodical documentation of experiences and events which, when taken as a whole, may be seen as the most effective manual for self-development.

It is also vital to keep a record of one's daily life so that changes in consciousness can be seen in a human rather than abstract context. Variations in physical circumstances, moods, events, all should be included in one's magickal diary.

Asana and Equipoise

In the Hatha yoga system of development, a series of physical positions or 'asanas' are used as an aid to concentration. Many of these require much time and effort to master, and, outside the Hatha yoga methodology as a whole, can be mainly disregarded. The essential teaching is simple: that by adopting an alert but relaxed posture in the body, an alert but relaxed mental state may be more readily achieved.

The asana selected is a matter of personal choice, and of physical prowess — most people find the full lotus position more than a little uncomfortable without lengthy prior training. However, whatever the position adopted, two major rules apply.

One: that the spine should be kept straight. The energy of the kundalini serpent, which is stimulated by occult exercise, flows up the spine. By maintaining a straight spine the energy may flow unhindered. On whatever level of reality this doctrine is viewed, from our experience, meditation while in a 'sloppy' asana tends to create tension in the body/mind relationship, and even leaves the unfortunate student with a headache.

Two: the position must be maintained without effort. Whilst keeping the spine straight, it should be perfectly possible to sit, or even stand, and allow the body to relax. A complicated asana of advanced Hatha yoga is of no virtue if you can only sit in it for a few minutes.

For the student there are four basic asanas which may be of use, these are shown in Figure 7.

130

Shiva Asana

Half Lotus

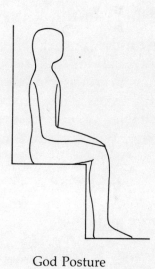

God Posture

Thunderbolt

Figure 7. Four basic asanas

In any of these positions the head should be tilted slightly upward, while the tip of the tongue rests behind the top row of teeth. This is to reduce the flow of saliva into the mouth and reduce the necessity to swallow. A hard pillow or mat may be used to raise the head slightly (as in the Shiva Asana) or to prop up the buttocks (as in the Thunderbolt Asana).

Other considerations are common-sense. Before attempting any exercise it is wise to have emptied the bowels and to have an empty stomach. Digestion of food and liquids tends to take up much of the body's energy, and so it is advisable to leave at least two hours from eating to practice.

Watchers in the Wings

As with the lying-down exercise described above, the first step in magickal training is not to try to effect some dynamic change in your self but rather to learn to observe what already exists. This can easily be accomplished by adopting a suitable asana and performing a simple 'Mahamudra' exercise, which consists of the following:

1. Adopt the desired asana, spine straight, with the body poised but relaxed.
2. Allow thoughts to flow through your mind; do not attempt to hinder the train of thoughts, let them rise and fall as they will.
3. After a few moments observe your thoughts. Stop your mind and retrace the train of thoughts which has come through your mind.
4. Allow other thoughts to well up but do not follow them; let them pass as if you were watching waves on the ocean.
5. Return to letting thoughts come and go as they will. Repeat the above practice as many times as you are able.

Most students find that they can increase their practice from five minutes to half an hour or more over the course of two weeks' regular exercise. The aim is to be aware of the flow of your own thoughts but not be a slave to them. This is a difficult technique to master and should be continued throughout one's magickal career. Magick without meditation is only half magick; even the greatest athletes must continue to train in the techniques they learned as beginners, or risk losing the edge that makes them great.

Paranayama

Breath animates the body and, according to occult doctrine, does so not just by imparting oxygen to the tissues but by imparting energy at other levels of being also. Control of the breathing mechanism is an ideal way to demonstrate that the individual can control and use a process which is, for the most part, unconscious. Paranayama, the yogic term for breath control, can be used in many ways. One example of this is the 'White Light' exercise which we have frequently used.

1. Adopt a suitable asana.
2. Relax your body and mind by concentrating on your breathing. Breathe normally; do not attempt to force the breath or change your natural breathing pattern at all. Focus your attention on the gradual ebb and flow of breath through your lungs.
3. As you breathe in, preferably through your nose, imagine your breath as a brilliant white light permeating your lungs and flooding the whole of your body with invigorating energy. Feel the light refreshing and rejuvenating your body and mind.
4. As you exhale, preferably through your mouth, imagine your body being cleansed of any impurities or unbalanced energies. Visualise your exhaled breath as coming from the whole of your body, not just from your lungs. You may wish to imagine it as a murky grey light dissipating as you expel it from your body.

5. Continue this exercise as you breathe in and out until your body feels purified and your mind relaxed. As you feel the practice taking effect, you may observe the exhaled light becoming gradually brighter until you are breathing white light when inhaling and exhaling.

This exercise provides an excellent means of entering a profoundly relaxed but alert state of mind. It is also useful for focusing or centring the body/mind complex. This practice may be used as an aid to developing the visualisation ability, an ability central to much of modern occultism. It is important to realise that the word 'visualisation' is a broad term and need not refer to the ability of maintaining a picture in the mind's-eye. Perhaps a better term would be 'Organised Imagination', for instance in the above exercise one may 'see' the white light, on the other hand one may simply feel its presence and effect. The process of feeling/visualising/imagining the white light will ideally become automatic, much as when riding a bicycle the subtle shifts of weight necessary to balance the rider become, after practice, unconscious.

It is important for the student to treat any exercise on its own merits. A common mistake is to try to apportion mystical properties to the white light itself, or indeed to anything else. It may or may not be true that imagining white light purifies and animates the subtle centres of the body. The point is that the exercise, properly performed, will apparently produce this effect. To quote Crowley (*Liber O vel Manus et Sagittae* — in *Magick*), 'Gods, Spheres, Planes, and many other things . . . It is immaterial whether they exist or not. By doing certain things certain results follow; students are most earnestly warned against attributing objective reality or philosophical validity to any of them.'

ELEMENTS OF THE SELF

Meditation, in the sense of observing the naturally occurring thoughts in the mind and developing 'one-pointed awareness', may be seen, symbolically, as the centre of the circle. Radiating from the centre of the circle are the four elemental forces, which, in terms of self-development, must be developed in a balanced, step-by-step way. All aspects of the self should be developed simultaneously. It is easy to develop and learn only the skills and abilities which have a natural appeal to the individual. This is the primary failing of the 'do only what comes naturally', school of thought. Intellectual types tend to be immediately attracted to the Air skills of analysis and acquisition of conscious (i.e. mainly written) knowledge. Emotionally sensitive people tend to be attracted by the Watery aspects of development, such as developing an awareness of energy flow in themselves and their environment. To develop as a whole person, one who already possesses an Airy nature will need to work on their Watery, emotional nature, and vice versa.

EARTH EXERCISES

In classic occult tradition the power of the magickian associated with the element of Earth was 'To Keep Silence'. In one sense this silence refers to the ability of the individual not to act but to receive impressions from the inner and outer environments. In basic terms, exercises pertaining to the element of Earth are those which concentrate on developing an increased appreciation and understanding of the universe through experience. Keeping an accurate magickal diary is, in one sense, an Earth exercise. By keeping a record of one's development, the student is able to observe personal changes. Thus the diary is akin to the magickal weapon of the pentacle which symbolises the sustaining and nourishing forces of the universe from which others grow. The diary highlights, if written and analysed properly, the courses of action the student should undertake in further training.

The principle of Earth-based exercises is this: surrounding us is the manifest universe, which we perceive by two routes, one conscious and one unconscious. Our conscious perceptions of reality depend on our senses, and spring from our sense of 'I', that is independent consciousness. One is only able to perceive the existence of a table because one is separate from it; one cannot perceive one's own face except by virtue of having a reflective surface to create its objective reality. Our sensory organs are limited by their specialisation, for example humans cannot observe ultra-violet light because of the eye's construction, unlike certain insects. Humans tend to overlook, or 'screen off' from consciousness, much of the information our senses provide us with. This process is, in the main, a function of the mind rather than the physical limitations of the sensory organs. For instance, a person may well be able to see the colour red but will often 'overlook' the astonishing tones produced by the sunset because they are not relevant.

Unconsciously all are intimately connected to the environment, by the flux of the seasons and corresponding changes in the hours and intensity of the sun's light, by the effects of the moon on the flow of blood in the body, and so forth. We tend to overlook these tides which link inner and outer reality thinking them 'not relevant'. The essential goal, therefore, is to sharpen the physical senses of the individual and make them aware of the tides which link the self to the environment. The exercises given below may be said to fall, broadly speaking, into the Earth category. Some of those given are suitable for individual work and some for use within a structured training group. In any event it is best if a lone student can find at least another, if not a more experienced magickian, with whom to exchange notes and discuss training and results.

136

Walking A Route

The student selects a route that is often travelled, and walks along it. This is particularly effective if the journey is usually taken by car.

While walking, the student tries to be intensely aware of the elements which constitute the journey: the sound of the wind in the trees, the colours of the buildings, the smell of the air, etc.

Touch and Taste

The student selects an item of food, such as a bar of chocolate. This is consumed, concentrating attention on the sensation: the visual form of the chocolate, its smell, taste, texture and the sound as it is eaten.

This exercise has many variations. The student may take a lemon and pinch of salt and become aware of the difference in flavour between them, then more subtle taste variations, such as between different wines. The same practice may be used in developing the sense of touch, as with the use of fabrics, hessian, velvet, silk, etc.

Active Listening

At any point in the day the student takes a few moments to be aware of the surrounding sounds: the murmur of heating systems, the ticking of a clock, the pulse of one's own heart.

Associated Smell

The student obtains a variety of perfumed oils or incenses. The associations for the student with each smell are then explored. For instance, on burning pine resin the student may recall a visit to a particular forest, etc. New smells, such as the unusual scent of opoponax, may be found to provoke feelings of sadness, repugnance, happiness, or even fear;

the reasons behind these associations are, at this stage, not relevant but all responses, or lack of them, should be noted.

Spaces Between

The student spends a week observing in a negative manner. That is, not seeing a leafless tree but rather the spaces between one branch and the next, not seeing the letters in an advertisement but rather becoming aware of the areas between each character, each line, and so forth.

Observation of the Seasons

Over the course of a year, the student becomes aware of the changing seasons. Careful note is taken of the lengthening and shortening of the hours of light, the order in which plants appear from the earth, the variation in the frequency and type of rainfall, and many other such occurrences.

People Watching

By spending just one day wandering around a town, the student can gain vital insights into the nature of human behaviour, and therefore his or her own nature. Gesture, method of walking, dress, make-up, habits — all should be observed as if the student were an alien investigating a newly discovered life form.

Selective Observation

The student selects a category of items from the immediate environment, such as 'things that are read' or 'things that are cuboid'. An attempt is then made to pick these items out, as rapidly as possible, at any given time, in any environment. One variation is for the student to select a key word, such as 'watch', then whenever this word is heard, is spoken, or written, the process of selective observation is activated. More complex categories may also be experienced with 'things that make me happy', or 'things I would like to own'.

Visual Memory — Kim's Game

The student asks a friend to place a series of objects on a tray. He or she then gazes at the objects; they are covered after six seconds and the student attempts to recall them all. The order in which the objects are recorded is worthy of detailed examination, as are the objects forgotten. A variation of this exercise could be for the student to attempt to recall all the items in the refrigerator, or objects in a car's glove compartment.

Earth means experience, at all levels, from observation of the way the seasons change, to the way a child develops, to the way a computer operates. The magickian should never be divorced from even the most mundane facets of the universal whole.

WATER EXERCISES

The power of the magickian associated with water is 'To Dare'. In practice, this daring manifests itself in a willingness to reach out and sense, psychologically and emotionally, the forces in the universe.

The moon is associated with the elemental force of water, with the ebb and flow of forces through the individual, with psychic ability, dreams and sensitivity as a whole. As the earth is the sustaining environment in a physical sense, so water sustains at an emotional and psychic level. In the simplest terms, earth is the body, water is the soul. The moon is closely related to this elemental force for it governs the tides of dreaming and emotion, and represents the astral plane. From this point onwards, the exercises may be seen as being conducted in various levels of reality: Earth equals physical; Water equals astral; Air equals mental; Fire equals spiritual.

Here the magickal record becomes a dream diary, recording the subtle interplay of ideas, worries, inspirations and hopes, as reflected in the individual dreamscape. Dreams serve as a barometer of the subconscious mind, and their analysis may be used as an excellent tool for developing self-knowledge.

In a human context, the Water element involves relating to others at a non-verbal, empathic level. Water is the ocean which links the human and non-human islands together. As this ocean ebbs and flows, so levels of sensitivity change; areas of each island are concealed or revealed. In magickal development, the aim is to understand these tides which are often described in terms of transferences of energy, and then to learn how to use them.

Working with emotional forces is notoriously difficult. It is easy to read too much into any given emotion, particularly before the Air process of analysis is fully appreciated. For instance, a man, interested in magick, may walk into a room and immediately find himself uncomfortable in the presence of a woman wearing a tweed skirt. As a budding magickian he may put this down to some fanciful psychic energy. However, it may simply be that the woman reminds him of a teacher he disliked in school, and that the energy is a product of his own half-forgotten childhood memory.

The watery powers of the magickian allow him or her to open up to energies of any type as required. A thorough grounding in the power of the Earth element, detailed above, should mean that the student will not be swamped by impressions, for Water is also the element of illusions and this fact must always be borne in mind.

Psychometry

The student holds an object, such as a watch, ring, or necklace, or places the hands on an object, such as a crystal stone, or brooch. The student then relaxes and allows impressions to flood into consciousness. Some of these impressions may be pure fantasy, others may have some greater meaning.

The Ritual Bath

The student begins by running a warm bath, perhaps scented with some appropriate oil, such as ylang-ylang, jasmine, or rose. A bath is then taken, preferably by candlelight. The student feels the water cleaning, relaxing and washing. The water is experienced as a warm envelope of pleasure and calm.

Word Association

To allow unconscious imagery to well up to consciousness, the student plays word association games. These may be done with a friend most successfully, or by opening up a book at random, or even by the use of a simple computer program. The method is simple: a word is given and the student immediately gives a response, free of conscious deliberation. The replies to words given should be recorded and any obvious trends in response and the length of time considered.

Animal/Plant/Colour

The student selects a person, again preferably at random and attempts to associate them with an animal, a plant and a colour. These associations should be completely free and not born of long considerations; the student must *feel* rather than think the answers.

141

Dream Work

The student attempts to gain full awareness of the dream-scape by attempting a series of exercises in the generation of 'lucid dreams', dreams where one is conscious of dreaming. One technique for this is for the student to gaze at the hands each night before going to sleep and mentally programme, 'I want to see my hands in my dream.' Upon dreaming, the 'shock' of seeing the hands may awaken the mind to the level where the student may still sleep but may take charge of the dreamscape and indulge in any adventure or fantasy desired.

The student also keeps a detailed record of all dreams, written immediately upon waking. Dreams are then considered at any point in the day. This is especially effective when faced with an unusual situation during the day. By remembering a dream at such a moment, many insights may be gained into the fluidity of reality and perception.

Allowing time to daydream is also important, and a record should be kept of the alterations in awareness found during these periods.

Lunar Changes

The student makes a record of the phases of the moon and observes if these phases have any noticeable correspondences with feelings, events, etc. Gazing at the moon also forms an effective lunar meditation. The student may decide to organise life into a lunar pattern, for example undertaking new projects and being creative at the new moon, harvesting and completing work at the full moon, stripping away old or outmoded elements in the waning moon, and generating new ideas at the dark moon.

Bodies of Water

Swimming in, touching, or observing different bodies of water is an effective exercise. The difference in feeling inspired by the sea, waterfalls, lakes, pools, should be experienced, as should the 'moods' of water, thundering waves, raindrops, mists, calm waters, etc.

AIR EXERCISES

To the magickian the power of the Air element is the power which permeates and analyses all other magickal data. The ability of the magickian associated with Air is 'To Know'. In relation to Water, the power of the Air element manifests as analysis (Water expresses emotion, Air examines and qualifies emotion). Alone, the element of Air is associated with communication, mainly in verbal or written form.

The nature of knowledge implies the ability to use the analytical faculties of the mind. The magickal diary of the student becomes a means of profound self-analysis. The record serves as a logical map of self-exploration, detailing past moves and suggesting future developments. The element of Air follows that of Water, so that the preceding principle of feeling is swiftly replaced by the principle of scrutiny.

In learning about the nature of the Air element, the individual begins to see that logical thought is not opposed to magick but is intimately a part of it.

A vital ingredient of the 'Air Mystery' is the study of correspondences. Correspondence structures are chains of thought which the magickian uses to break down the whole of the universe into separate, though connected units. Each force in the universe can, according to the doctrine of correspondence, be described in terms of associated ideas. For most purposes the universe is divided (analysed) into various compartments, such as the four elements, seven planets, twelve zodiac signs, twenty-two cards of the tarot Major Arcana, and so on. Thus the force, called 'Mercurial' is associated with a series of ideas and concepts: trickery, swiftness, intellect, communication, androgeny — and a series of symbolic forms: the Egyptian god Thoth, the metal quicksilver, the incense of mastic, the plant hazel, the Hebrew letter Beth, opal, Wednesday, etc.

This practice is intended to allow the magickian to see the universe as an interconnecting web of correspondence chains. In practical terms, correspondences provide a logical consistent map of the universe, both as micro and macrocosm. To this end, the doctrine may be used to analyse information which is 'felt'. For instance, a pathworking may be undertaken which leads to a Mercurial area of the psyche. By analysing the symbolism and impressions gained in the vision it may be established how much of the pathworking was the genuine result of entering that level of reality and how much was fancy or falsification. Correspondences may be used as a logical method to stimulate particular areas of the psyche. Thus, if the magickian wishes to invoke the force of Mars, then he or she would compose a ritual using Martian correspondences: Mars is an active force and so the ritual would be of the active sort, perhaps involving dancing or drumming, rather than quiet meditation. Incense containing ginger and dragons' blood could be burnt; five red candles placed on the altar, which would be set in the fiery south of the circle.

Knowledge of the doctrine of correspondences takes many years of study. It is, however, the principle of the doctrine that is important and not whether there is really any link, subjective or otherwise, between constriction, Saturn, lead and myrrh. Correspondence is, in fact, a method of communication which is the central feature of Air. Communication implies the ability to take an 'idea' as perceived through the senses and to divide it into a series of words. This series of words must be formulated in such a way that it is intelligible to the listener.

Communication also implies the ability to generate a situation where there may be an interchange of information; language is useless unless it facilitates such an exchange.

144

Gathering Knowledge

Of the many ways open to the student to gain information, reading is the most important. Books, and not just occult books, should be obtained from libraries, shops, second-hand stalls and the like.

The student should develop a wide range of knowledge not only about the history of the Qabalah but also about geography, biology, physics, feminism, in short whatever interests the student, or may be of use.

Films, concerts, video games, computer systems, all present a potential goldmine of information. It is not necessary to memorise all the information provided but rather to learn how to tease out the essential logic or concept behind any given experience.

The Correspondence Game

The student, having studied the basic principle of correspondence should try various exercises to extend the knowledge of this subject. One example of this would be an adaptation of the Animal/Plant/Colour exercise (see page 141). Yet now the student must find a reason for each correspondence and develop an internally consistent logic. Thus if a bird is Mercurial because it has wings, then a flying fish must also be Mercurial — unless, that is, there is some flaw in the first attribution of birds.

The student should begin by making correspondences between natural objects (mountains, turtles, oak trees), then man-made objects and emotions (hate, envy, automobiles, watches). Different correspondence systems should be used: initially the four elements, then the planets, the zodiac signs and even the sixteen sub-elements (i.e. 'Earth of Fire', 'Water of Air', 'Air of Air', and so on).

Analysis in Speech

The student notes how his or her speech, and the speech of others, is formulated, what expressions are used, what exclamations are adopted, and which words are repeated. The use of language can be analysed, both in the spoken and written word, and thus the peculiarities of its form discovered. For instance the word 'sow' is confusing, when written, until defined by other words, for example, 'the sow is a female pig', or 'we sow the fields with maze'. Equally, there are curious expressions such as '. . . well to tell the truth', which would seem to imply that everything the speaker has uttered up until those words was falsehood!

Paradoxical Notions

Experimenting with simultaneously holding paradoxical notions can lead the student to a greater understanding of the nature of analysis, duality and 'truth'. For instance, global starvation vs fast-food gluttony, infinitely big vs infinitely small, the will to live vs the will to die.

Suspending Belief

The student selects something that is believed to be true, such as 'the world is round', or 'eating meat is morally wrong', and attempts to suspend that belief. Thus, if it is believed that eating meat is immoral, the student should consider the idea a reasonable possibility, perhaps even eat some meat. The exercise is conducted until the relativity of the previous position can be fully appreciated, so that the other point of view can be clearly seen.

Syntax of the Magickal Language

The Qabalah provides one of the most remarkable representations of the forces which animate the universe, expressed for the most part, in a logical Air-based way. The student must study the Qabalah and repeat the correspondence exercises in the light of that system. The system of gematria which arises from the Qabalah is by far the most sublime, complete and logical system of correspondences. The symbolism and meaning of numbers should certainly be studied.

FIRE EXERCISES

The ability associated with the element of fire is 'To Will', and it is the will that is at the core of all magick. The occult meaning of the term is different to that usually understood. Will is often confused with 'wishes' or 'desires' or even 'whims'. In *The Book of the Law* it is said that, 'Pure Will, unassuaged of purpose, delivered from the lust of result is in every way perfect.' The will of the individual is a line of least resistance through the universe, and this is referred to as the 'Path of the True Will'. Magick provides a means by which this course may be discovered and pursued.

Fire is action. At the beginning of training, the actions of the student are like a series of flickering flames, then, by development, the flames are focused into a single ray, like that of the laser. This singleness of purpose may be seen in the mountaineer, the great chess player, the poet, the banker, in fact in anyone who finds their natural niche in the scheme of things, and is able to fulfil that position to the utmost.

In the context of Fire, the magickal record becomes a crucible in which old ideas are burnt up and new ideas formed. The magickian begins to see the record not as something dead and gone but as a moving growing thing, a furnace in which the old self has been consumed by experience, impression and communication, and replaced by something rich and strange.

The power of Fire means the ability to direct, to focus and to be. Fire balances Air because it implies action without analysis, rather Fire represents synthesis. As Air breaks down elements, so Fire, as in the analogy of the laser, concentrates and focuses. As fire is spontaneity and action, it cannot operate as a quality when it is divided against itself. For instance, when one sets out to perform a ritual, the magickian must analyse and intellectualise, forming appropriate chains of thought, through the medium of correspondence, to invoke the required force. However, once in the ritual it is pointless to continue the analysis; the Fire force takes over and the ritual is done to the magickian's fullest ability. Just as the footballer, when faced with the opportunity to score a goal, does not stop to analyse the implications of his act, he just acts.

An example of the way Air/analysis can thwart Fire/will may be seen in the simple action of throwing a ball. If a person is told that a ball is going to be thrown to him he will begin to analyse the forthcoming act. As a result he may become nervous or try to predict the way the ball will be thrown. If this happens, then the chances are that, when the ball is finally thrown, he will be so bound up in conscious thought he will drop it. However, if he is surprised by the pass he is more likely to catch the ball properly. It can be more effective to return a ball in tennis when the player only has time to react, than to serve when time to consider the action is available.

In a personal context, Fire represents inner strength and also the genius of the individual. Fire energises and activates but it also destroys, and this duality is important. It is easy for the student to build up to the 'All powerful Adept', imagining Fire to be about glory for the ego, forgetting that Fire also implies transformation. Similarly the magickal diary is not just a record of development, it is also a tool for transformation. The magickal record displays as much where the student has failed as it does where success has been achieved. The disciplined attitude to practice, which the student must maintain is a form of Fire, as is the inner strength that will see the individual through the difficult and often painful initiations into hidden levels of the self.

Objective Anger

The student selects an object, one for which no major personal associations have been made, such as a stone. The student then becomes angry with it, raising this anger to an irrational pitch against the stone, which should be seen as the embodiment of all that is loathed, feared and found abominable both in him or herself and others. Anger is expressed in whatever way, by hitting the stone, burning it, or shouting at it. At first there is a natural tendency to feel self-conscious about this practice but after a few attempts it can produce some quite explosive results.

Guarded Speech

Selecting a commonly used word, such as 'I', or habitually repeated phrase, such as 'actually', from everyday speech, the student should refrain from using the word for at least a week. Each time he or she fails in this task a record of the event is kept and the circumstances surrounding its occurrence.

Seeing the Fire Within

The power of Fire manifests in many forms. The student can attempt to see the 'fire' in various things: the shooting forth of buds in May, the 'power dressing' of the business woman, the rebellious hairstyle of the punk, the carefully focused Fire of the cat ready to pounce.

Pyramid of Power

The student makes a list of all desires, and any associated qualities, abilities and material objects. These are then arranged in order of importance, perhaps using a Qabalistic scheme, noticing how one leads to another.

Positive Moving

The student should make a note of each movement made during a week which is not positive. There should then be an attempt to correct this in the following week. If in the habit of walking slowly with short paces, these should be changed to a wide-stepping rapid stride. Any psychological changes which this new positive movement provokes should be noted.

Affirmations

The student takes an area of life with which difficulty is experienced, such as finances. A series of statements are written down which represent the student's present beliefs about money. For example:

'Money is necessary because . . .'
'If I was rich I could . . .'
'I wish I had . . .'
'I can't find the money to . . .'

He or she then looks back over these sentences and attempts to replace them with positive messages. By doing so an attempt is made to replace one set of mental programmes with others.

Magickal Oaths

The student takes a 'magickal oath', that is an oath which should be within one's power to perform but not necessarily with ease. The oath is written out, solemnly repeated and then either carried on one's person or put in a conspicuous location. Whatever the oath is, it must be complied with to the letter. Thus, if the student takes the oath, 'I will not touch alcohol for one week', the oath must be abided by in just that form. Therefore the student must not touch alcohol — no 'medicinal drams' nor even the use of alcohol based nail-varnish remover; moreover a week is 168 hours long, not from 6 p.m. Sunday 20th to lunchtime on Sunday 27th.

Reclaiming Functions

The student makes a conscious effort to take over a function that has been left for others to perform, such as making bread or mowing the lawn.

The Elemental Assembly

Bringing together the elemental forces within the self forms the fifth element referred to as Spirit. This gathering together of the elements is a life-long task. Phil Hine writes in his book, *Walking Between the Worlds*, '. . . It is an eternal journey that reaches into all of us: the Fool, Luke Skywalker, me, you, everyone. It never ends: I don't believe in utopias, perfection or 'True Selves' which are eternally bathed in bliss. The striving is the important bit.'

EVERYWHERE THE CENTRE

Ritual, like any other aspect of magick, requires practice. The problem is that ritual is such a potent method of transformation that it would be unwise to do it 'just to see what happens'. This difficulty is resolved by the use of 'focusing ritual'.

A focusing ritual consists of a simple rite which is intended to have the effect of harmonising the elemental forces within the self. Such a rite is often employed before and after a major rite as a centring exercise. It may also be used as a type of psychic protection. For instance, before undertaking a tarot reading, the reader may undertake a focusing exercise to stabilise personal energies. Then, confronted with an anxious and sorrowful client, he or she will not feel emotionally drained after the reading. A simple example of this would be when the magickian removes the furniture from the room in which it is intended to work. The furniture is not 'evil', nor yet is it impossible to perform a rite in the middle of coffee tables and chairs. However, the clearing out process helps one to 'psyche-up' for the work ahead. There is also a corresponding mental effect, 'As I clear my room of obstructions so I clear my mind of undisciplined thoughts.'

The protective aspect of focusing ritual is often overplayed. In fact in classic magickal parlance these rites are referred to as 'Banishing Rituals'. This is misleading. It is not the aim of a focusing ritual to banish hostile entities or forces. Such forces are rarely encountered, but rather to create an equivalent of the magickal circle around the individual — to give the magickian a space into which a harmonious range of forces can be called that will be energising.

The student should begin by studying the various rituals already in common use, and analysing the elements which are common to all methods. Focusing rituals commonly employed today come mainly from the Golden Dawn and the work of Crowley, such as 'The Banishing Ritual of the Lesser Pentagram' and 'The Star Ruby'.

It should soon become apparent to the student that the essence of these rites is as follows:

1. Organised imagination of the single source (Spirit).
2. Dramatised expression of Spirit (or chaos) made manifest.
3. Balancing of these forces into the concept of polarity.
4. Invocation of the four elemental forces.

152

5. Absorption of these forces and identification of the magickian as the centre of the circle (or *Axis Mundi*).

6. Repetition of steps 1 to 3.

The exact formulation of the focusing rite will depend upon the belief system adopted by the individual. Yet in all cases the purpose of the rite is to establish the magickian at the centre of his or her universe, and to energise that universe with a unified energy. It is advisable for the student to practise performing a focusing ritual each day for at least three months. This may seem somewhat excessive but the duration of a focusing rite need not be more than fifteen minutes. Regular practice at this level will also serve to provide the student with an actively enhanced centre from which to experiment with more extreme exercises. By consciously harmonising the energies flowing within the self, a focusing rite may be used as an earthing. In occult terminology, an exercise, such as psychometry, brings the individual closer to the quarter of Water in the circle. Continuous use of a focusing ritual helps redress the balance and prevents the individual losing their centre and becoming drawn exclusively to the 'watery' parts of the universe.

The two rituals below are examples of focusing rituals. The first is a much simplified version of the 'Banishing Ritual of the Lesser Pentagram', the second shows how the same principles may be applied according to the individual will, in the example given by using Egyptian symbolism.

No focusing rite should be too complex, and the student is always best advised to begin by using a simple tried and tested method before evolving a more personal one.

The Simplified Lesser Pentagram Ritual

No special preparation for the rite is necessary. The magickian may wish to use a wand or dagger for drawing the pentagrams but the fingers (usually the fore and middle finger) of the hand are quite sufficient. The place in which

153

the rite is conducted is of no importance although the magickian should attempt to make it as free from clutter and distraction as possible. It would be appropriate to push furnishings or other articles of modern living out of the way to produce a relatively clear space.

Comfortable clothing should be adopted by the magickian to allow him or her to relax and feel free of restrictions.

1. The magickian begins by standing in the centre of this space, facing east. A sphere of brilliant white light is visualised at the forehead, representing the formless glory of Spirit (the Tao, the Ain Soph Aur, the Is), touching the forehead as this is done.

Speak: 'Unto Thee.'

2. Draw the hand down to the breast and 'imagine' the white light flowing downwards into manifestation. (This may be seen inwardly as the white light forming 'black flames', a magickal paradox exemplifying that these things are 'perceived' not conjured as pictures in the mind's eye.)

Speak: 'The Kingdom.'

3. Touch the right shoulder and 'imagine' the first polarity of the yin/passive/feminine.

Speak: 'And The Power.'

4. Touch the left shoulder and 'imagine' the second polarity of yang/active/masculine.

Speak: 'And The Glory.'

5. Clasp the hands together across the breast, and 'imagine' the coming together of these forces with the central pillar, i.e. the forehead and breast, the union of spirit in matter.

Speak: 'To the Ages. So mote it be.'

6. Then move towards the quarter of the east, or simply turn to that direction, and draw the invoking pentagram of Earth with the wand, dagger or hand (see Figure 8).

Feel the influx of the element of Air into the sacred space and into oneself.

154

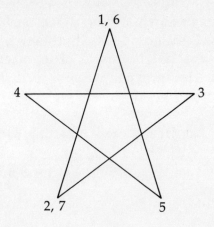

Figure 8. The Invoking Pentagram of Earth. It is drawn with six strokes. The dagger, or wand, is then thrust through its centre on completion

7. Move towards the south and repeat this process feeling the influx of the element of Fire.

8. Thence to the west and the element of Water.

9. Thence to the north and the element of Earth.

10. Return to face east and stretch out the hands so as to form the body into the shape of a cross.
   Speak: 'Around me the elemental powers and I am their centre and their Union.'

11. Repeat steps 1 to 5, the simplified 'Qabalistic Cross'.
   The rite is ended.

This ritual may seem enigmatic, however the rationale behind the actions is simple. The magickian identifies with the basic principles in the universe (unmanifest potential Spirit, manifest kinetic matter, and the active and passive expressions of this duality). The 'observable' results of the interplay of these forces are then invoked as the four elements. The magickian makes an assertion as the focus of their harmonious union, and then draws the forces inwards by repeating the Qabalistic Cross. In this way the rite is like the pulsing of the heart muscle. The magickian builds, contracts (steps 1 to 5), expands (steps 6 to 9), reaches the fullest extent (step 10) and withdraws again (the repetition of steps 1 to 5).

A simple rite like this is often exacting for the beginner because it relies so much on qualitative forces (for instance how does one visualise 'glory'?). Yet for some it is a most effective tool.

An Egyptian Focusing Rite

Preparation: as above. The whole point of any focusing rite is to concentrate the power of the self and to create a virgin area in the mind.

1. The magickian stands facing east. Raise the hand above the head, palm uppermost. Visualise Nuit, goddess of Infinite Space. Imagine the infinite void of space above.

Speak: 'Nuit is above me.'

2. Draws the hand down to the breast, imagining the line described by the hand as a beam of energy coloured deep blue. On the breast visualise the symbol of Hadit, god of the 'atomic seed' principle, in brilliant scarlet.

Speak: 'Hadit is within me.'

3. Point the hand outwards to the right, still facing east, and visualise Nephthys, goddess of darkness, magickal power and protectoress.

Speak: 'Nephthys to the right of me.'

Then withdraw the hand to touch the breast and feel the power of the goddess flowing inwards like a breath.

4. Repeat the above by holding out the hand to the left. Here the goddess Isis, Mother and Lady of all life, is visualised.

156

Speak: 'Isis to the left of me.'
And again feel the breath of the goddess as the breast is touched.

5. The magickian then makes the sign of 'Osiris Slain', arms flung outward to form a cross.
Speak: 'May their Breath fill my nostrils.'

6. The magickian moves to the east and draws the ankh symbol in the air. Visualise the symbol as composed of pale yellow light, and visualise the ape, symbol of Thoth, god of writing, communication and intelligence.

7. Then turn to the south and repeat the process, visualising the ankh composed of scarlet flames. Visualise the hawk, symbol of the god, Horus, god of fire, strength and vengeance.

8. Thence to the west, the symbol seen as moving, flowing lines of blue. Visualise the serpent, symbol of various gods and goddesses, representing the secrets of death and rebirth.

9. Thence to the north, the symbol being visualised as organic green in colour. Visualise the scarab, symbol of the god Khephra, Lord of Light in darkness, or putrefaction and growth, and of the earth.

10. Returning to the east, make the sign of 'Osiris Risen', hands crossed upon the breast.
Speak: 'I am the Balance of Maat, the Breath, the Essence of all that Is.'

11. Repeat stages 1 to 5.
The rite is ended.

This ritual relies far more on visualisation for its effect, and the images consistent in a particular culture. However, the rubric is identical.

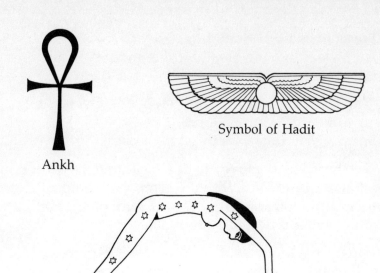

Ankh

Symbol of Hadit

The goddess, Nut

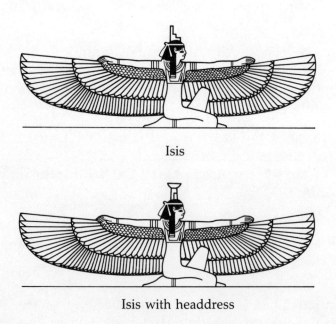

Isis

Isis with headdress

Figure 9. Magickal symbols

The symbolism of such a rite needs to be carefully studied. As we have seen, it seems easy to misconstrue the nature of a deity (see Chapter 3). Construction of a rite like this should be a careful process but attempting to forge one's own focusing rite may provide many valuable lessons in itself.

In conclusion, it is important to stress that magickal training is in no way, if properly applied, intended to remove the spontaneity of the individual. Rather it is intended to shape natural instinct and intuitive insight into a productive tool.

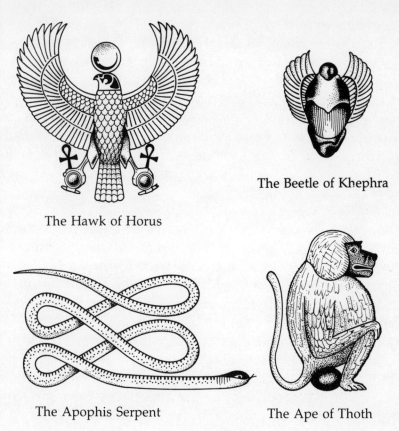

The Hawk of Horus

The Beetle of Khephra

The Apophis Serpent

The Ape of Thoth

CHAPTER 11
ISSUES ARISING

The following is an article first published in Destiny *magazine in the autumn of 1986. A glance through the 'contact' section of any occult magazine will reveal advertisements placed by people interested in becoming involved in Wicca or magick. In many cases the initials 'RHP' or 'LHP' are used. These abbreviations stand for Right-Hand Path and Left-Hand Path respectively. Most contacts state 'RHP only' or 'no LHP groups', and so on. The reason for this is that many people mistakenly believe that the Right-Hand Path is identical with good and the Left-Hand Path with evil.*

Where then do the terms 'left' and 'right' come from, and if they don't imply good or evil, what do they represent? These expressions can be traced back to the early Tantric cults of southern India, which embodied the fruits of the equatorial African mystery cults. 'Tantra' has many meanings. The word itself refers to Indian sacred texts written on every subject from astrology to yoga. The Tantras base their teachings on the theory that the universe is formed by the interaction of opposite but complementary forces. These energies are symbolised by the union between god and goddess. Tantra describes the use of sexual union, breathing exercises, yoga and other techniques that can help the individual be in touch with this cosmic union. Tantra's use of male/female archetypes leads to the magickal division between feminine and masculine qualities.

It is important to understand that these qualities appear in *both* sexes. Sensitivity is a 'feminine' characteristic but can occur in both men and women as can logic which is a 'masculine' trait.

In the Hebrew Qabalah this division of cosmic male–female interplay was continued. The Hebrew, Tree of Life, as every occultist knows, is a system that involves the planets, tarot cards, and so on. The Tree is also divided into three pillars, or paths to the godhead. It is from the Qabalah that the confusion about the RHP and LHP arises.

The Qabalah's three pillars are given symbolic colours: black (left pillar), white (right pillar) and the grey or rainbow-hued central pillar. The pillars are also given symbolic genders, the left and right pillars being female and male respectively. This system was based on the Divine Union cosmology of Tantra.

Having established the origin of the terms we must look at the reason that the Left-Hand Path became considered malific. The LHP became associated with evil simply because of its association with the feminine aspect of godhead. In early cultures, the concept of Good versus Evil was unknown. Everything was a sacred manifestation of the godhead that had to be respected and understood. The concept of good and bad was given force by Zoroaster, a Persian religious teacher who lived about 600 BC. He reasoned that the universe was the battlefield of an eternal struggle between good and evil, concepts he personified in the beings Ormuzd and Ahriman. The influence of Zoroastrian thought was felt in many cults, later in Jewish religion, Mithraism and early Christianity.

The repressive patriarchal cults feared the feminine aspect of the godhead mainly because this was the aspect most associated with magick, psychic powers, and so on. The establishment knew these powers were difficult, if not impossible to control. Because of this a mass hysteria was built up against the feminine aspect. This can be exemplified by the symptomatic repression of women in many patriarchal

161

faiths. Not only were women suppressed but the feminine power in both genders was frowned upon. Men had to be aggressive and dominant and not express any feminine emotion such as sensitivity or passivity. In a magickal context, this can be shown by the way that the lunar god, Set (incorporating many 'feminine' qualities), who in Egypt symbolised initiation and the power of the LHP, became degraded into Satan, the Devil who fought with God.

The LHP deals with the feminine archetypes. Its main symbol is the image of the goddess. Any belief system which emphasises the development of feminine powers is using the LHP. Therefore Tantra, and much of modern Wicca and Paganism are based on the mysteries of the Left-Hand Path. Perhaps it would be more accurate to say that any occult way should aim towards the Middle Path. Magick, or indeed any self-development method, should serve to balance both masculine and feminine traits in the self.

The LHP is the path of magick and the occult sciences, rather than the RHP which deals with logic and philosophy. Once the universe had been divided up into good and bad, as male and female, so other concepts developed moralist characteristics. Black, night, the moon, etc. (all LHP symbols), were considered evil. People began to fail to see the necessity of these elements in the cosmic whole. In the same way that complementary medicine approaches the body as a whole so in ancient times the occultist saw the world as a whole being.

Humanity understood that darkness was necessary for light to exist in the same way that winter is necessary for summer. The patriarchal cults degraded the LHP and so these symbols became shunned. For example, the symbol of the pentagram, the five-pointed star used as the sign of Wicca, has been subjected to the good/evil misinterpretation. Symbolically, the pentagram with one point up represents the way that the elements, Fire, Air, Water and Earth, issue from the top point of Spirit. The pentagram

162

with two points up shows us that by experiencing all the elements we may come to understand the godhead. In this orientation it is not a symbol of Satanism or evil forces. Correspondingly, Tantra uses sex to bring enlightenment about rather than ascetic rejection of the material world. Nature and matter are not evil, they are as divine as Spirit.

This prejudice even shows up in the iconography of Western films, where the Goodies wear white hats and the Baddies black hats! The mystery of the Middle pillar is that Black and White are not good and evil. They are complementary opposites as are the god and goddess, and they must be balanced and both understood in order to allow the individual to progress.

If the concepts of good and evil are based on false assumptions, how then are we to construct a moral code of conduct? It is important to realise that good and evil are subjective concepts.

In this context, a way to draw up a moral code is by understanding the law of karma. Karma is not an inbuilt system of fair play in the universe where good deeds are rewarded and bad actions punished, as we have described in Chapter 3. Karma is the law of cause and effect. It states that any energy ultimately returns to the sender. It is for this reason that all reputable occult groups discourage the use of curses, as any magickal action ultimately exhibits a boomerang effect. The moral of the law of karma is that you should not do anything the consequences of which you are not prepared to accept. Any moral decision you take must be taken with the law of karma in mind. This is particularly important in magickal work. With the confusion between the LHP and RHP some types of magick have come to be regarded as white magick or black magick. No magickal distinction is so clear cut. For example, healing is generally thought of as white magick. This involves the female concept of working with the whole — female therefore LHP.

If someone is dying of old age, then healing is the last thing they need! If it is their time to depart the earth level then forcing that person to stay could be positively harmful. In this situation a simple rite to allow them to die in peace and without pain would be far better. The important thing to consider in any situation is the fact that whatever you do will ultimately affect you. The philosophy of 'do unto others as you would have them do unto you' is quite correct. For example, if you decide to do a magickal work for somebody, you must consider the situation. Work out if you *need* to influence the situation, and if so act to the best of your ability — mindful of the consequences of your act to others, and ultimately to your self.

Any sort of self-development path leads to internal confusion, where moral guidance must be sought from the higher self. The laws of society are important but in the end it is what your heart feels is right that should prevail. An understanding of the self requires that both the right and left-hand paths are understood. Then the self can come to the realisation of the cosmic dance of the god and goddess, the union of complementary opposites which sustains the universe.

THE QUESTION OF HIERARCHY

One major dilemma facing anyone who wishes to set up a magickal group is the problem of the structure of hierarchy that should exist. Groups are made up of individuals who have particular talents and gifts. It is natural that some people will exhibit those traits we have come to recognise as leadership qualities. These qualities stem from life-experience, confidence, and an ability to turn the energies of various individuals upon a particular goal. In terms of occult leadership, there are less well defined criteria. Many people are forced by circumstances (the higher self) into undertaking the role of High Priest or Priestess. Often the classical leadership qualities are missing in these individuals, or are not present in the same way that they are in other people.

The role of High Priestess or High Priest can only be performed by one who has the required levels of self-understanding and magickal knowledge, abilities which cannot be easily quantified.

Different groups require differing power structures: a feminist group has a different system from a formal magic-kal order, which is in turn different from a loose-knit net-work of occultists. It seems that the best power structure for a magickal group able to work with a similar system to the one we have described, is a tribal one.

In a practical sense this is impossible to fulfil in an urban, government-centralised society. We started out our own occult careers with high ideals of groups in which all the members had an equal say.

In a short space of time it became obvious that individuals needed training even in simple aspects of magick, such as the knowledge of symbols, visualisation techniques, etc. At a much later stage, we found it necessary to delineate clearly between an inner working circle, and an outer training group comprised of greater numbers.

We have found it necessary to impose a minimal fee (which goes towards our time, incense, candles, and so on) on those in awareness training. The training itself, however, is not charged for. This simple practice helps to discourage those who are not sufficiently interested in occultism to make a small sacrifice of money. It is unfortunately true that one has to treat the majority of applicants as 'children' as even qualities such as dedication, self-motivation and fore-thought, are sadly missing from many people. Through the process of training, only those really interested can have access to the inner circle.

Even in such a controlled pyramidal power system prob-lems can become apparent in the inner group. Thus the High Priest and High Priestess must be ultimately respon-sible for discipline.

Here is one of the most vivid demonstrations of the concept of Perfect Love and Perfect Trust. In the end, the whole group must trust the judgement of the High Priest and High Priestess.

Whilst we are in favour of other organisational forms being adopted, the pyramidal power system seems to be the most effective form. This need not imply rigid discipline to the point of stagnation. In occultism any individual is free to change any commitment to another individual or group. If a member is unhappy with the way a group is run, then they can leave.

An occult order should be formed of true individuals (literally 'not divided') working towards a common aim. In Aeonic terms the adepts must be 'loners' like the Horus hawk, a group, like the bees of Ma'at, and linked between these states by the goal of magick, symbolised by Set — the dark side of Horus and Maut — the dark form of Ma'at as the goddess of the stars.

Perhaps when our social structure changes then the most appropriate hierarchy for a magickal group will also change.

THE TEMPLE

The location of the temple is today a choice dictated more by practical considerations than by any specifically magickal constraint. It is preferable if the temple can be situated in the house owned by the High Priestess as she is the core of the group and therefore should be the custodian of the inner group's meeting place.

By using the term 'temple' we do not mean to say that a particular room need be set apart from any others and used solely for magick. A living room will serve just as well or a large bedroom. It is preferable to keep the temple alive with energy by making sure that the room is used and not kept locked. Even if you do have space for a specific temple room then, for instance, also make it a library. In this way it will remain part of the house and its energy will not stagnate.

Ideally the temple should be suitably large enough to allow space for dancing but not so large that it feels cold or empty.

The question of temple decoration requires careful consideration, perhaps the best course to follow being what feels right for the group concerned. Neutral colours are appropriate for the walls and floor, so that any coloured altar clothes, robes or drapes, appear more dramatic. As for paintings, ritual equipment, icons, and so on, our attitude is to keep these simple. Too much occult clutter only serves to distract the attention and makes the temple look messy. Seasonal flowers are always a good idea but again it is better to err on the side of scarcity rather than over-abundance.

The layout of the altar will depend on the type of work being done and the current of magick being worked by the group, but it is always preferable to have a broadly symmetrical altar spread.

If the focus of the temple is clear, then the focus of the mind is clear. If possible, weather permitting, it is helpful to hold a rite, particularly a Sabbat, inside the temple and then after the consecration of the first wine to move outside. Here a bonfire can be lit, and dancing, jumping the flames and general fun can let the energy of the rite go to work. Positive enjoyment helps magickal power earth itself, and releases the participants from the seriousness of a ritual — after all, if you can't enjoy magick what can you enjoy?

Magick works outside the net of linear time, so in order to take full advantage of this, work in areas that have been virtually untouched by time. Such locations (stone circles, old houses, natural forests) are also often natural power points and sites of previous occult work. Some of the best working sites in Britain have lost this timeless quality owing to the pressures of tourism — Stonehenge is a prime example — and the fact that no real magickal work is allowed to take place within them. Whilst we agree with conservationists that places like Stonehenge should be protected from vandals, not allowing genuine occultists to use the site is squeezing the life force out of it.

On the question of magickal tools, we tend to keep to the Wiccan standard of having one pentacle, bell, sword, etc. We do have more than one wand because different wands can have vastly differing occult functions, such as a banishing wand, a phallic wand, a wand used for 'Art' magick, and so forth.

A general diagram of the circle and altar is reproduced here in Figure 10.

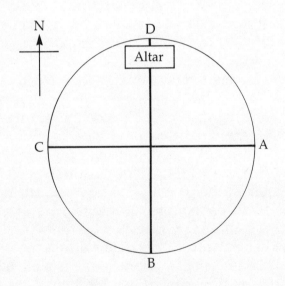

Figure 10. The Magick Circle and altar. Key: (A) East; Element, Air; Weapon, Wand; Quarter candle colour, yellow, (B) South; Element, Fire; Weapon, Sword; Quarter candle colour, red. (C) West; Element, Water; Weapon, Cup; Quarter candle colour, blue. (D) North; Element, Earth; Weapon, Pentacle; Quarter candle colour, green or brown

THE PROCESS OF INVOCATION

The idea of invoking the presence of a godform into a particular individual is probably as old as humanity. As we have said in Chapter 3, gods exist outside the mundane conciousness of an individual, and reside within the confines of the higher self. Figure 11 explains further the reality of a deity in relation to the process of invocation. Here we have used a seven-fold division of occult reality as an aid in explanation. It must be remembered that levels of reality blend into each other and there are no hard and fast frontiers between them. Each plane has its own function, and is not more or less important than any other.

The process of evocation is fundamentally identical to invocation. The idea that evocation raises evil spirits from below the earth and invocation calls upon good forces from above, is based on Zoroastrian dualism. Perhaps the only occasions that the term evocation can be used with any real meaning is in when either Qabalistic, Klippothic or necromantic work is being performed.

The process of invocation falls into four broad categories, these are:

1. Invocation by one magickian on another.
2. Self-Invocation.
3. Invocation by 'Assuming a Godform'.
4. Invocation of an entity outside any particular individual, also known as 'Invocation into The Circle'.

1. Invocation on, for example, the Priestess by the Priest, is usually conducted within the circle, and is the most common form of invocation used within Wicca as a whole. It is not possible to explain exactly how the force is brought into manifestation within the Priestess.

Externally, little in the way of physical movement need be done by the partners in this operation; the Priestess takes an open receptive position, such as standing or seated with the arms raised and held apart, palms open. The Priest stands

LEVEL		REALITY	DEITY TYPE: EXAMPLES	CONTACT
UPPER	SPIRITUAL	The infinite potential of the macrocosm	Force	E
LOWER	SPIRITUAL	Archetypes of whole principles	Mat, Ishtar, Cerridwen	
UPPER	MENTAL	Archetypes of specific principles	Bast, Aries, Baldur	D
LOWER	MENTAL	Simple archetypes with specific areas of operation	Angels, Watchtower lords	
UPPER	ASTRAL	Forms related to particular racial groups or locations	Elementals, various myth types	C
LOWER	ASTRAL	Personal godforms, 'created' forms	Demons, astral guides	B
ETHERIC		Popular conceptions of force, imbued with power by use	Exoteric images of all gods	A
PHYSICAL		Kinetic material expression	Form	

Figure 11. Planes of reality and their functions. Key: (A) Contact by religious worship, prayer, etc. (B) Contact by demonic 'external' invocation, dream control techniques; construction of 'personal' beings, such as talismanic entities, familiar spirits. (C) 'External' invocation of godforms; invocation of 'place' spirits. (D) Invocation of godform into the circle of the occultist's own persona. (E) Some invocatory methods but mainly ecstatic states

or kneels before her, raises his hands and lowers them until they are resting on the Priestess. Mentally the Priestess must place herself totally in the control of the Priest. She will know what force is to be invoked and so will be able to open herself up to a certain wavelength of power. The Priest, aided by the rest of the group, must call on the force in question. The group's visualisation of the required force must be crystal clear and identical. This last point is important, for if there is any discrepancy within the group image then the current invoked will be marred.

As we have shown in our rituals, it is preferable to invoke both the god and goddess into manifestation in order to balance the circle.

Only those with a high degree of magickal understanding should undertake the process of invocation, it is not simply a psychological game. If the receiver of the invocation is not completely open to the force being drawn in, then only the negative aspect of the force invoked will manifest, even if this is not desired.

Physical actions in magick are generally unnecessary. They do however help to focus the will, and in a ritual to keep the chain of occult communication open from macrocosmic to microcosmic levels. Physical actions in a rite help hold the participants on the earth level. Ritual is sharing. Its aims can all be achieved mentally but a physical rite assists the sharing of an individual experience within a group structure.

Each magickian has a personal godform to which they are most attuned. If this form is invoked on a receptive person, then the godforce will manifest easily and dramatically. Whilst under the influence of a particular godform, the individual retains their normal personality but certain areas are accentuated, and this direct link with the higher self changes the energy that the magickian radiates and increases it in relation to the nature of the godform and work in hand. Some invocations are accompanied by changes not only at a personal, occult level but also on the physical plane. Changes in voice and the aura are common but perhaps more dramatic is the process of shape-shifting that often follows an invocation. 'Shifting' takes the form of changes in the face and occasionally the whole body. This occurs when the magickians personal godform is invoked, particularly if the form is of an atavistic nature. An observer may find that one moment they see the Priest as a serpent then a human; these forms shift back and forth until the magickian is neither serpent nor man but a dynamic union of the two. The eyes of the Priestess may appear to change to those of a cat and her face develop a pointed feline appearance.

An atavism is an animal form around which most primitive godforms were constructed, such as Anubis the jackal, Arachne the spider, Thoth the ibis or ape, etc. Such forms are linked directly to the roots of the subconscious because during our evolution we have passed through these states and still retain their nature and powers in the recesses of our minds.

Atavistic forms also refer to those that have yet to evolve, many of which research suggests are to be based on primitive animals such as the snake and similar beasts. Invocation allows the adept to awaken the abilities of these animals both 'real' and symbolic, and by inference those of the animals we shall be.

2. Self-invocation involves the magickian in fulfilling both the role of the receiver and the director. It has a number of uses both in and outside a ritual. An example of the ritual use of self-invocation is given in our Imbolc rite. Outside a ritual, self-invocation can be used as a means of activating the psychic circuitry to aid the physical being.

This ability was demonstrated by the occultist and artist Austin Spare. Spare was required to lift a heavy weight, which, under normal circumstances, he would have been unable to move. To accomplish the task, Spare invoked the atavism of a tiger on himself using his system of sigil magick. He was then able to perform the task.

Self-invocation is most easily performed if the magickian's personal deity or atavism is involved. Again it is impossible to describe the exact process but basically it involves the occultist calling on the godform and then opening the psyche in order to receive its essence.

3. Assumption of a godform is commonly used by ceremonial magick. It involves steeping one's self in the mythos of a particular deity until the deity becomes part of the occultist. If the magickian wished to assume the goddess Artemis, he or she would first research and learn all there is to know about this goddess. Then would begin the process of becoming her. The magickian would have to dress, eat, talk as Artemis, and slowly would begin to be absorbed into the goddess. This procedure culminates with a great ritual of invocation. The effects of this type of invocation are numerous. The period of assumption generally lasts at least as long as the period of preparation, the longer and more profound the preliminaries the longer the manifestation. Even when the invocation has apparently ceased, flashes of the Artemis persona will still occur sporadically.

Only occasionally is this type of work of any real use. It offers greater duration but not necessarily more power than the previously described invocation types. People should be their own gods, not reflections of other deities.

4. Invocation into the circle acts in the same way as the first two described above but the godforce, instead of taking up residence in one individual, permeates the whole structure of the group. An example of this is the invocation to the elemental watchtowers performed in casting the circle. The elemental forces are not consigned to particular people but are invoked to channel their respective powers into the circle. This type of invocation can be done in many ways, and the changes brought about by it will be felt to some degree by all the participants. Again, if one individual is particularly sensitive to the invoked force, it will tend to manifest most potently through them. This method of invocation allows all those in the circle to be affected by the power of the godform.

Invoking particular forces into given areas of the circle, such as a triangle described in or outside its perimeter, is also possible. This technique is more akin to the traditional images of invoking angels and demons. Invoking entities in this way is possible but a degree of magickal understanding is necessary to hold such a force in one area. The aim of this type of work is to constrain the entity so that objective communication can take place. This method is often applied when trafficking with forces commonly known as demons. These include messenger forms such as Aiwaz, Lam, or Daemash, or godforms which have particular functions, such as Hauges, Azrael and Oriens.

IN CONCLUSION

A number of other elements that form the fabric of Serket have not been dealt with in this book. Most of these elements would only be of interest to those working this type of occultism either using the format presented here or some other expression of it.

Figures 12 and 13 (see pp. 175 and 177) are selected correspondences used by us which directly relate to the four-fold year and the three realms that we have adopted, which may help to show how the practical nature of Serket does not mean that it is without the wealth of symbolism apparent in other esoteric paths.

We have chosen diverse correspondences, some of which will be apparent to the less experienced reader and some of which will have more meaning for the experienced occultist.

The outer work of the occult movement at present must be the reformulation of systems, the creation of new

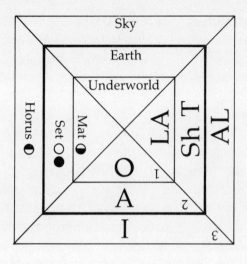

Figure 12. Correspondences for the three realms

theorems which will form the expression of magick over the coming Aeon. It is not the task of present adepts to attempt to formulate the 'Practice' element in any system. Crowley did not construct detailed rules for the performance of Thelemic magick, neither does the Wiccan *Book of Shadows* contain precise ritual instructions. In esoteric terms, today's magickians must engage in the Scorpionic process of analysis to 'plough the earth' from which the synthesis of magick will be born.

With the new acceptance of magick, in the form of complementary medicine, hypnosis and the like, into the fabric of conventional science, a new difficulty may arise. Humanity has a basic need to know and comprehend, perhaps a need born out of 'fear of the unknown'. The danger is that occultists may be side-tracked into attempting to rationalise magick into a scientific structure. The very action of occult power is shrouded in mystery. It is the artistic element of magick that serves to lift from its logical elements (correspondences, numerology, etc.) a vibrant current of energy.

As Crowley remarks in *Magick Without Tears*, 'Magick is the Science of understanding oneself and one's conditions. It is the Art of applying that understanding in action.' Quantum theory may come close to appreciating the methodology of the occult but it cannot describe magick as a whole. It is the 'Art and Science' status of magick which reveals this truth. Magick is a description of the whole universe. Whilst, for example, science can construct a piano and mathematically fashion a scale of notes, it cannot provide the creative fire for the composition or performance of a great concerto. Esoteric thought cannot be compartmentalised — magick is the illusive animating force of the cosmos.

An understanding of magick needs both the keen mind of the scientist and the ability to accept mystery.

Throughout this book we have attempted to put into words ideas that are at once simple and complex, apparent and arcane. Experience, such as that of a Sabbat rite, creates the doorway through which understanding may flow. The understanding gained will be appropriate to the individual's level and path of development. Knowledge may be gained by study but it is the event of initiatory experience that provides understanding.

Opinions within the ranks of occultists are split as to the nature of the next Aeon's manifestation. In political, scientific and social terms, prognostication is extremely difficult. Most adepts agree that a basic aspect of the new Aeon's structure will be that of dualism of thought.

The Gaia hypothesis argues that the earth is a self-regulating unit in which each species has a role to fulfil. Elements in this theory are identical to the macrocosm–microcosm principle in occultism. This attitude also coincides with the esoteric view that all things are conscious but at different levels, and that groups of closely associated life forms develop a group unity.

Present social conditions demonstrate one of the more peculiar and important aspects of the new age. The new era is not, unlike the preceeding two Aeons, under the direct

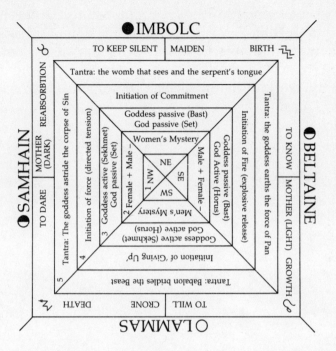

Figure 13. Correspondences for the four major Sabbats. The correspondences in the outermost block of the illustration apply to both Sabbats, and thus are orientated to the quarters rather than the sub-quarters. For example, the goddess at Beltaine partakes of the aspects of the maiden and the Light Mother. Following this at Lammas, she is both the Light Mother and the Crone, and so on

auspice of a single current. The approaching Aeon will be under the rulership of both Horus the sun/son and Maat, goddess of truth and justice. The facts surrounding this curious state of affairs are detailed in many other works, but in the present day the action of these forces is clear. Materialistic conservatism, epidemic disease and the like, are the beginning of the analytical process of Horus; the synthesis of Maat has yet to emerge in the world. When these two currents are united by adepts, then we shall see the emergence of the new age proper.

The magickian is the guardian of esoteric understanding and the knowledge of the keys required to tap the hidden depths of the mind. It is because of this that occultists must put their own house in order. Humanity has, and may again, rely on the occultist to preserve it.

It is the work of the magickian that manifests in society's outward form. Magickians create the world they inhabit, not vice versa. Ours is the responsibility.

BIBLIOGRAPHY

Bord, Janet & Colin, *Earth Rites*, Book Club Associates by arrangement with Granada Publishing Ltd., 1982.

Budge, E.A. Wallis, *The Book of the Dead*, Arkana, 1985.

Budge, E.A. Wallis, *The Gods of the Egyptians Vols. I & II*, Dover Publications, 1969.

Bradley, Marion Zimmer, *The Mists of Avalon*, Sphere Books, 1983.

Campbell, Jospeh, *The Masks of God — Primitive Mythology*, Penguin, 1984.

Carroll, Pete, *Liber Null*, Morton Press, 1987.

Casteneda, Carlos, *The Teachings of Don Juan*, Penguin, 1979.

Crowley, Aleister, *Magick*, Routledge & Kegan Paul, 1983.

Crowley, Aleister, *777 and Other Qabalistic Writings*, Samuel Weiser, 1982.

Crowley, Aleister, *The Book of The Law*, (also known as *Liber AL vel Legis*), Golden Dawn Publications, 1990.

Crowley, Aleister, *The Book of Thoth*, Samuel Weiser, 1980.

Davies, Paul, *God and The New Physics*, Chaucer Press, 1983.

Dawkins, Richard, *The Selfish Gene*, Granada, 1978.

Farrar, Janet & Stewart, *Eight Sabbats for Witches*, Robert Hale, 1981.

Farrar, Janet & Stewart, *The Witches' Way*, Robert Hale, 1984.

Fix, Wm. R., *Star Maps*, Octopus Books, 1979.

Gardner, Gerald B., *The Meaning of Witchcraft*, Aquarian Press, 1959.

Grant, Kenneth, *Aleister Crowley & The Hidden God*, Muller, 1973.

Grant, Kenneth, *Cults of The Shadow*, Muller, 1975.

Gray, W.G., *Seasonal Occult Rituals*, Helios Books, 1976.

Gray, W.G., *The Ladder of Lights*, Helios Books, 1968.

Grian, Sinead Sulce, *Brighde's Fire*, Privately Published, 1985.

Hine, Phil, *Walking Between The Worlds*, Pagan News Publications, 1989.
Lawrence, Louise, *The Earth Witch*, Collins, 1982.
LeShan, Lawrence, *How To Meditate*, Thorsons, 1985.
Leyland, Charles G., *Aradia: The Gospel of the Witches*, C.W. Daniel, 1974.
Lindholm, Charles & Cherry, *The Erotic Sorcerers*, Science Digest, 1982.
Mumford, John, *Sexual Occultism*, Llewellyn, 1975.
Nicholls, Peter (editor), *The Science in Science Fiction*, Book Club Associates, 1983.
Oken, Alan, *Complete Astrology*, Bantam Books, 1976.
Richardson, Alan, *Gate of Moon*, Aquarian Press, 1984.
Shuttle, Penelope & Redgrove, Peter, *The Wise Wound*, Gollancz, 1978.
Slinger, Penny & Douglas, Nick, *Sexual Secrets*, Arrow Books, 1979.
Stewart, R.J., *The Underworld Initiation*, Aquarian Press, 1985.
Symonds, John, *The Great Beast*, Panther Books, 1963.
Thompson, William Irwin, *The Time Falling Bodies Take to Light*, Rider & Co., 1981.
Valiente, Doreen, *Witchcraft for Tomorrow*, Robert Hale, 1978.
Wilson, Colin & Woodruff, Una, *Witches*, Dragons' World, 1981.

RESOURCES

Magazines

Chaos International, BM Sorcery, London, WC1N 3XX.

Circle Network News, PO Box 219, Mount Horeb, WI 53572, USA.

Fire Heart, PO Box 462, Maynard, MA 01754, USA.

Pagan News, Box 175, 52 Call Lane, Leeds, LS1 6DT.

Talking Stick Magazine, Suite B, 2 Tunstall Road, London, SW9 8DA.

Shaman's Drum, PO Box 2636, Berkeley, CA 94702, USA.

Organisations

The Fellowship of Isis, Clonegal Castle, c/o PO Enniscorthy, Eire.

EarthSpirit Community, PO Box 462, Maynard, MA 01754, USA.

EarthBirth, 523 Lighthouse Avenue, Santa Cruz, CA 95060, USA.

Talking Stick, Suite B, 2 Tunstall Road, London, SW9 8DA.

Invoking Earth has grown into RootMagick which is the core group of the Dark Star international guild. Invoking Earth, Box 21, 46 Woolmans, Fullers Slade, Milton Keynes, Bucks. MK11 2BA.

INDEX

If you have enjoyed reading this book, other titles in the Quantum list will be of interest. These include:

The Dream Lover, Transforming relationships through dreams
by Les Peto

Dowsing For Health, The applications and methods for holistic healing
by Arthur Bailey

Life Cycles, The astrology of inner space and its application to the rhythms of life
by Bill Anderton

Psychic Sense, Training and developing psychic sensitivity
by Mary Swainson and Louisa Bennett

The Survival Papers, Applied Jungian psychology
by Daryl Sharp

Applied Visualisation, A mind-body programme
by James Lynn Page

Astrology's Complete Book of Self-Defence
by Robert Parry

The Healing Hand Book, Discover and develop your healing power
by Patrick Butler

Ask your bookseller for full details on the complete range of Quantum titles, or write directly to the publisher, W. Foulsham & Co. Ltd., Yeovil Road, Slough, Berks. SL1 4JH